DRESS TO IMPRESS

How to Look & Feel Your Best Every Day

Brigitte Nioche

Illustrated by Tina Liu

JANUS PUBLISHING COMPANY
London, England

First published in Great Britain 1994
by Janus Publishing Company
Edinburgh House, 19 Nassau St.
London W1M 5DF

Text Copyright © Brigitte Nioche 1994
Illustrations Copyright © Tina Liu 1994

**British Library Cataloguing-in-Publication Data.
A catalogue record for this book is available from the
British Library.**

ISBN 1 85756 147 3

Cover design Linda Wade

Printed & bound in England by
Antony Rowe Ltd,
Chippenham, Wiltshire

TO MY BEST FRIEND,
MY MOTHER

Contents

Introduction

How to Look and Feel Your Best Every Day

How good looking you are, and how confident you feel about yourself is not a matter of how fashionable you are, or of how much money you have, or even of how beautiful you are, it is a matter of how well you can present and package yourself.

Yes, packaging is what sells most products and when it comes to looking good, you are the product and your clothes are the wrapping.

The belief that there are no ugly women, just women who do not know how to look attractive, is truer today than ever before. Today there are no limits on what a woman can wear. There are no do's and don'ts, and not even the fashion designers impose any particular look on today's woman. Our options are varied and plentiful and if a woman cannot find her particular look among them, she can only blame herself.

Without over-emphasising the importance of appearance, don't forget that the biggest asset you have in life is yourself and you must use it to its best advantage. The French philosopher Voltaire once said: 'Dress changes the manner'. That was true in the eighteenth century and it is still true today. Think about how good you feel when wearing your favourite outfit – or how you want to fade into the wall when you are wearing something you don't like.

Choosing the right clothes can make you look and feel your best everyday. However, it does not happen by itself. It takes a little time and more importantly, a commitment to yourself.

Having made the decision to find out HOW TO LOOK AND FEEL YOUR BEST EVERY DAY you might ask, 'Now what?'

The first step is to take inventory of yourself. This is not an exercise in scrutinising your defects. The point is to look at your body objectively and make a list of your assets: my legs are good; I could probably wear my skirts a bit shorter. Maybe my hair shouldn't be pulled back, or maybe it would look more feminine a little longer. What about makeup to bring out my eyes?

To see what you like about yourself, you need – besides an open mind – a full-length mirror. Stand in front of it and try to imagine that the person reflected there is someone else. This way your good points become more apparent. Being more objective will make you more generous. You will give yourself credit for what you have instead of being over-critical.

Start with your hair. Does it frame your face the right way? Is it too short to do so? Or, if your hair is long, would a shorter style make it appear thicker and more sensual? Would more frequent brushing add the life that is missing? When looking at your face, it might occur to you that make-up could improve it. If you are not used to wearing any, or if you don't want to look made-up, relax: having good make-up that enhances your face does not mean a heavy, painted look. It can be very subtle and still create the effect you want.

Now to your body. In order to know what to do about a large bust or thin arms, you must first be aware of your assets and liabilities. And to help you to get to know yourself well, I would like you to fill out the chart overleaf. Standing in front of your full-length mirror, pull in your stomach and stand straight. Start with your shoulders; don't accuse them of sloping when bad posture is the culprit. Examine yourself carefully and circle the appropriate adjectives.

Now that you have completed the list, check it thoroughly. You will find that you have more assets than defects. And don't feel

HEIGHT:
WEIGHT:
HAIR COLOUR: **DRESS SIZE:**

SHOULDERS:	Broad	Narrow	Sloping Just right
NECK:	Long	Short	Fair Just right
BUST:	Big	Small	Fair Just right
ARMS:	Heavy	Thin	Fair Just right
WAIST:	Big	Small	Fair Just right
TORSO:	Long-waisted	Short-waisted	
STOMACH:	Protruding		Fair Just right
HIPS:	Wide	Narrow	Fair Just right
DERRIÈRE:	Big	Flat	Fair Just right
LEGS (length):	Long	Short	Fair Just right
THIGHS:	Heavy	Thin	Fair Just right
LEGS (below knees):	Heavy	Thin	Fair Just right
HANDS:	Small	Large	Fair Just right

My best feature(s):

What I don't like about myself:

depressed about something like heavy thighs; most defects (or what appear to be defects) can be corrected or minimised through diet, exercise, better posture, better care, or more attention to detail. There are very few things that are impossible to correct, and even those are easier to live with once you know them. Being aware of your body will help you buy the clothes that will make you feel and look more attractive and confident.

1

The Importance of Colour, Prints and Fit

COLOUR

Colours have a great influence on your femininity. They send out all kinds of messages. Think of black. It is known to look sexy when worn as lingerie; on the other hand, as the colour of a judge's robe it imposes authority. White is known to stand for purity, but a white bikini on a tanned body looks very appealing. It is impossible to say that one colour is more becoming than another. What makes the difference is the person who is wearing it, and how the colour contrasts with her skin.

The contrast a colour creates is very important because contrasts bring out vitality, and vitality is associated, even if unconsciously, with attractiveness. For example, a blond dressed in black or a brunette in beige will look more vibrant than the reverse. A blond dressed all in beige or white will project a monochromatic look and appear a bit lifeless. Only strong make-up can improve the situation. (I can speak from experience here, being a blond myself.) If you are blond and wish to look alive, make sure that you wear your beige suit with a dark-coloured blouse or sweater, such as black, brown, rust, or burgundy. A white or pastel shade will look well on a brunette with olive skin.

Colours affect how we look and how others see us, more so than style. (We say, for instance, that a dark colour is authoritative – without even mentioning the style of a garment.) Colour is the first thing in our wardrobe to which we should give our attention. No style or design can make up for a lack of colour co-ordination, or for a shade that does not compliment a person's complexion, personality, or lifestyle.

LOOKING AT WHAT YOU HAVE

Many fashion designers never follow any guidelines; ignoring all the rules, they trust their instincts. I am asking you to do just that. Look at yourself and the colours you wear and decide what you like and what you feel good in. If you answer that you really don't know, now is the time to find out. I know from working with women that there is hardly a woman alive who doesn't react when something looks well on her, provided she makes a real effort to notice. Therefore, the first thing I am asking you to do is trust your own judgment. When you are in doubt, the colour is not for you. If it were, you would have immediately responded to it in a positive way.

What you need to do now is work with your present wardrobe. Try on your clothes and look at yourself. Do you like what you see? Maybe you think: I never should have bought the burgundy blouse for the charcoal-grey suit – it's drab. Well, why not try the white blouse instead? See how much livelier that looks? The message here is that two muted colours don't enhance your appearance because your face needs more light.

NOTE	Never (if you wear make-up) try on clothes without make-up; the results will not be dependable.

Trying on all your clothes will help you learn more. You may find, for example, that navy isn't really a great colour on you; you liked yourself better in burgundy or grey. This exercise will prove that you do indeed know what colour is just right for you.

Since your wardrobe, like most wardrobes, doesn't contain all colours, now is the time to experiment with some shades you've never worn before. Most shops let you try on clothes before making a purchase. If, for example, lavender or charcoal grey are among those never-before-worn colours, find out now how they look on you. Remember not to listen to the salesperson – decide for yourself. Also, don't think that another style might make a difference. If the shade isn't becoming, another style won't make it more attractive. (To illustrate this point, think of the times you've tried on something and thought: 'If this were in a different colour I'd like it,' or 'The colour is nice but the style isn't for me.') You must consider the colour before the style. Never prejudge: try it on and look. If a blouse you want to buy comes in six colours, it's a good idea to try on several to see which is the most flattering.

Also don't forget that colours come in many different shades. While brown might not be appropriate for you, tan might be. Often we are too general in our assessment of colours. We don't consider the many different tones that exist. Beige is a good example: there are lots of different beiges. If a very light tone makes you look lifeless a camel tone might look smashing.

By the way, the richer and more unusual shades can often be found only in more expensive garments. The higher price might be worth it if the shade in question suits you especially well.

When shopping and trying to decide whether a certain colour is good for you, try to look at it in daylight. Artificial light changes colours. Go to the door of the boutique or to a window in a department store. If this isn't possible, check it at home. If you find it to be unsuitable, take the trouble to return it. Don't compromise when it comes to your looks. The contrary applies when buying an evening dress or a garment to be worn mainly in artificial light: try it on in that light. Many colours that look well in daylight appear drab or ugly in the evening.

NOTE

Once you have done your research, you will see that there are many colours that suit you. However, for practical purposes – budget, lifestyle, and easier co-ordination of your wardrobe – you will have to eliminate some.

Let's start with your budget. Your funds are probably limited, which means that you have to plan your wardrobe to get the most for your money – many different looks with relatively few pieces.

These pieces have to match any way you put them together. You cannot have both a navy-blue and black suit because they and their accessories can't be interchanged. The best solution is to pick two colours that suit you well and build your wardrobe around them.

Of course, if these two colours are red and royal blue, they might not fit your lifestyle, which is your next consideration. Red and royal blue would not be suitable as basic colours. They are noticed and remembered too easily by others and they are inappropriate in many situations. So you should concentrate on the neutral tones that suit you: black, white, grey, brown, beiges, navy, and so on. From these pick two for the basic items in your wardrobe, such as coats, suits, dresses, trousers, and skirts. Don't worry about being too monotone in your look, for there are endless variations and shades in these colours. Another advantage of basic colours is that you will never look out of place, either at work or in a more casual setting. Furthermore, you will never be overpowered by these shades. I'm referring not only to your complexion but also to your personality. It takes a certain bravado and energy to carry off flamboyant colours. Unless you have plenty of both, you will feel and look uncomfortable in, for example, a bright pink. You can see how true this is when you think of days when you don't feel well; don't you automatically choose a darker outfit? This comes from your unconscious desire to fade into the background.

NOTE | When you're tired, it's better not to wear black at all. Instead, put a lighter shade next to your face.

Now look at the bright colours that you found becoming. Just because they don't fit your lifestyle as basics doesn't mean that you have to live without them. You can wear them in small quantities: in a scarf, belt, blouse, bag, and, if you are daring, as the colour of a pair of shoes. Did you ever own a pair of red shoes? They go with more outfits than you realise. They brighten up a grey dress, a navy suit, or a black skirt. Red also looks very fashionable with beige; a red blouse can work wonders with a beige suit.

Another factor that can help you decide on a colour is the type of fabric. A heavy fabric projects a colour more strongly than a thinner, finer material. There seems to be more of it. Take yellow, for example. In a wool fabric, it will be too bright for most of us. But

4

the same colour in chiffon or silk is very soft and feminine.

Sometimes it happens that a colour unflattering to you is needed to complete an outfit. Let's say you have a tweed jacket with a little bit of green in it. A green blouse or sweater would certainly complete the outfit, but since green is not a good colour for you, choose a green skirt instead – it is far enough from your face not to be unbecoming. In other words, keep an unflattering colour away from your face. This type of compromise is sometimes necessary to extend your wardrobe.

Don't worry too much about the latest fashion colour. It is never the only colour to be worn, even if it is the dominant one of the season. If it is suitable for your looks and your lifestyle, by all means wear it. If not, don't feel too bad. Remember that looking terrific is more important than looking fashionable. **NOTE**

ABOUT BLACK

Black makes most people think of long evening gowns, of deep décolletages, of silk and satin – in other words, of elegance and sensuality.

Because black is the most important of all colours, it deserves some extra attention. Black is becoming to every complexion and suits every figure. It can be worn during all seasons and looks attractive in all types of fabrics. It is elegant, authoritative, sexy, and sad. In the late nineteenth century domestic servants, shopgirls, clerks, and elderly people of modest means were only considered properly dressed when in black. It can be worn equally well by men and women.

Black is a colour worn by rich and poor, by the clergy and by call girls. It can indicate positions of social standing high and low. It is both serious and worldly. It is *the* colour that is universally the most appropriate for most occasions. Most important, it never really goes out of fashion. Around 1930 Gabrielle Chanel brought out the famous 'little black dress,' which since then has never left us.

CO-ORDINATING COLOURS

Whenever someone asks me to describe the greatest error in dressing, I have to answer that it is the co-ordination of colours – or rather the lack of it. The other day I looked in disbelief at a young woman who was dressed like this: black coat, light grey trousers, beige shoes, blue cap, dark brown handbag, burgundy attaché case, and, to top it all off, striped gloves in bright red, yellow, blue, green, and mauve! From the various fashion components one could see that this woman purchased items of the highest quality but because of poor colour co-ordination she looked messy and unappealing. Unfortunately, this kind of dressing is not rare. Many women wear up to five or more different colours at the same time. (Just look around you.) In the winter the problem is worse, since people wear more clothes.

Women speak with respect of someone who is well co-ordinated: 'She's so well put together.' There is really no secret in looking that way. It just takes planning. The same day I saw Ms. Striped Gloves, I saw another woman who also wore a black coat, but her accessories consisted of beige handbag, a black attaché case, beige boots, black gloves, and a beige hat-and-scarf set. Everyone looked at her admiringly. She wasn't wearing anything special or outstanding, but what she did have on fitted together.

I am often asked, 'How can I learn to co-ordinate my wardrobe better? 'If you think about what you have in your wardrobe and only buy clothes that will fit into that colour and style scheme, you will have no problem co-ordinating your look.

Most of us know that brown goes with bone, and black with red. But for new ideas, fashion magazines are a real eye-opener. Study the way they combine colours. You would probably never think of wearing a royal-blue blouse with your tan suit, but seeing it in *Vogue* will convince you that it can look fabulous.

Since we all know that brown and beige or black and red go together, the following chart will help you to find some additional and more unusual combinations. Colours that harmonise well are:

Black and orange	Blue, scarlet and purple (or lilac)
Black and maize	Blue, orange and black
Black and lilac	Blue, orange and green
Black and pink	
Black and slate	Crimson and gold
Black and royal blue	Crimson and orange
Black, yellow, and crimson	Crimson and maize
Black, orange, and blue	Crimson and purple
Blue and stone	Green and scarlet
Blue and straw colour	Green and gold
Blue and maize	Green and orange
Blue and chestnut (or chocolate)	Green, scarlet and blue
Blue and gold	Green, crimson, blue and yellow
Blue and orange	

Lilac and crimson
Lilac and maize
Lilac, scarlet, and white (or black)
Lilac, gold and crimson
Lilac, yellow or gold, scarlet
and white

Orange and chestnut
Orange, blue and crimson
Orange, purple and scarlet
Orange, blue, scarlet and purple
Orange, blue, scarlet, white,
  and green
Orange, lilac and crimson
Orange, red and green

Purple and gold
Purple and orange
Purple and maize
Purple and blue
Purple, scarlet and gold
Purple, scarlet and white
Purple, scarlet, blue, yellow and
  black

Red and gold
Red, orange and green
Red, yellow and black
Red, gold, black and white

Scarlet and slate
Scarlet and blue
Scarlet and orange
Scarlet, blue and yellow
Scarlet, blue, black and yellow

White and scarlet
White and crimson
White and cherry
White and pink
White and brown

Yellow and chestnut (or choco-
  late)
Yellow and red
Yellow and crimson
Yellow and purple
Yellow and violet
Yellow and grey
Yellow, purple and crimson
Yellow, purple, scarlet and blue

Another source of inspiration are the combinations of men's clothing. The colours and prints used in men's wear are as appropriate for women as they are for men. Many women say they envy men because they always look well co-ordinated. The secret is that the colours used are fewer and stay mostly in the same colour family, with shirt and tie adding life and colour. This should translate for us into wearing neutral basics and adding colour with accessories: scarves, belts, and blouses or other tops.

PRINTS

To choose a suitable print that will enhance your colouring and personality is not easy. Many of them are too busy, too bright, or too large. Most men I know prefer solid colours. I was told: 'Prints make a woman look older'; and 'Prints make me think of curtains or tapestry.'

It's true that many patterns tend to make one look older, especially floral prints. (Maybe this has to do with memories of our grandmothers' aprons!) Other prints tend to overpower the wearer. While a woman client and I were shopping, we saw a dress made from a beautiful coloured floral material. She liked it so much that she tried it on. When she looked in the mirror, she kept admiring the dress, never looking up at her face. I asked her if she thought this dress did something for her. Now, looking at herself, she had to admit that the loud colours and the big print did appear overpowering.

Anyone seeing this woman would have noticed and admired the dress – but the wearer would never have been seen. In order to avoid being overwhelmed, choose a subdued print. A flattering print is one that is soft in colour or widely scattered.

What also helps to make a print more attractive is a quiet spot somewhere in the ensemble, like the trousers in this picture.

If a print is on the loud side, wear a solid colour next to your face and wear the print in the skirt, in the underside of a collar and cuffs, around a hemline of a skirt, or on the back of a dress. Here is a general rule that will guide you in your selection: if the pattern is small, the colours, can be bright and multiple, but as the print gets larger, the colours should become lighter or less frequent. For example, a small paisley print can be done in red and yellow on a blue background, but a large design should be more muted.

SOME GUIDELINES

BODY TYPES:	BEST COLOURS AND PRINTS:
If you are UNDER 5′ 5″ AND SLIM	• Light colours – since there is less of you, a small woman can afford these shades, and also prevent herself from being overlooked. • One-colour outfits – they give the illusion of length. • Solid colours – they don't overpower. • Prints – must be dainty and neat. Little floral designs or dots are suitable but only in subdued colours. Tiny all-over designs look best in tailored styles. • Stripes – only very fine ones, close together. Wide ones make a short woman look square.
If you are SHORT AND HEAVY	• Medium tones – for example, dark beige or camel. If you choose a two-tone outfit, buy one with the darker shade where you are heavier – either above or below the waist.

10

- One-colour looks – they will help you appear taller and slimmer.
- Pattern-on-pattern – this is better than a print in different colours. (Pattern-on-pattern uses small, usually shiny, squares, dots, or other designs in the same colour on a dull background. Found often in silk-like fabrics and knits.) If your figure is too full for prints, use them in the form of a trim on cuffs or collars or as piping on solid colours.

If you feel that you were short-changed because you are small, rejoice. Small women keep their youthful appearance much longer than tall women. Just think of your friends and compare. Doesn't Jane at 5 feet 2 inches look younger than Doris, who is 5 feet 9 inches?

NOTE

If you are 5' 5" TO 5'8" AND SLIM

- All colours – provided they are suitable for your complexion.
- Prints – medium-size in bright colours; larger designs in softer shades.
- Stripes – of medium size, not larger than 12mm wide and no farther apart than that.
- Dots – from very small to the size of a ten pence piece.

If you are MEDIUM HEIGHT AND HEAVY

- Dark shades – light colours only as blouses and accessories.
- Solid colours – are best so as not to emphasise weight.
- Prints – only in small, muted designs; nothing bright.

11

If you are OVER 5'8" AND SLIM	• All colours – but never too bright, as they would be too obvious.
	• Two-colour looks – they will break up the silhouette (a different colour top from the skirt).
If you are OVER 5'8" AND SLIM (cont.)	• Prints – no extremely large ones. A top with a small size floral design (with a solid-colour collar and cuffs or scarf) and a smaller design in the same colour family for the skirt would make a pretty outfit. This combination breaks up your silhouette in a subtle way.
If you are TALL AND HEAVY	• Stripes – these should be fine (about 2mm) and close together to avoid the pyjama look.
	• Solid colours – wear two at a time, rather on the dark side. With a dark skirt, for example, a rust-colour blouse would be more slimming than one in white. If it has to be light, cream or off white is better.
	• Dark colours – this must not only be black and navy, but can also be dark mauve, dark beige, khaki, dark red, and so on. (Dark colours do not really make you slimmer, but they do divert attention from the parts of you that you want to minimise.)
	• Prints – choose a medium discreet design that is widely

If you are TALL AND HEAVY (cont.)

scattered instead of close together in a soft colour. Avoid very small and busy patterns; they will make you look as if you are wearing a curtain. If you yearn to wear a print, limit it to a blouse worn under a jacket. Or choose a jacket with a print lining.

- Stripes – choose a fine one in two similar tones, such as light blue on white.

FIT

A good fit determines how smart you look. A bad cut distorts your figure, while a good one shows it to its best advantage. We read a lot about how we can hide and camouflage figure flaws – but why should the flaw always be us? Have you ever tried on a dress that you liked, but found that it didn't look right on you? You may have thought that something was wrong with your figure but the garment itself could have been the culprit. When the shoulders of a garment are a little too wide or if a sleeve is not set in well, the resulting pulls and puckers are unsightly. Unfortunately, with mass production of clothing, workmanship has declined greatly. Today, more than ever, time and money are needed to find the correct fit. You need time to examine an item thoroughly to see how it is made. And you need money in order to get a better fit and finish. Well-made buttonholes, carefully stitched hems and seams, pattern co-ordination and good fabrics cannot be found in cheap merchandise. The extra money you spend will pay off because your garment will last longer and will keep its good looks as long as you own it.

It is important to keep in mind that you will look better in clothes that fit well without distorting your figure. For example, avoid a jacket that makes you appear too large on top, a pair of trousers with a crotch so low that the length of your legs is reduced by a few

inches, or a halter-neck that gapes and thus distorts your bust-line. A halter-neck should fit snugly like the one in the picture.

NANCY'S PROBLEM

You may have trouble finding good-fitting clothes if you wear one size on top and a different one on the bottom. But don't be discouraged. What you feel to be a drawback might really be an asset. A client of mine found that out one day when we went shopping.

Nancy, a good-looking woman in her early thirties, was convinced that she had a big problem, since she was not a standard size. Her 'problem' turned out to be a size 38 bust with 36-inch hips – in other words, a very sensual figure and one that most women would give their right arm for. (The other way around – the pear-shaped figure – is much more common and much less attractive.)

Admittedly, it took time to find what we wanted. But we found a handsome, conservative blazer in a subdued black-and-white check, paying special attention to the fit over the bust. The lapels had to lie flat, and the jacket had to close easily without being too loose. Under it we chose a blouse that was slightly loose to avoid a too-busty look. The colour was fuchsia, lively but not too bright or loud. A straight black skirt completed the outfit. It was too long, so it had to be shortened to show the world that she had a pretty pair of legs. When we had finished our shopping, Nancy looked both business-like and feminine in her trim blazer and soft classic blouse. It was a change from her ill-fitting two-piece dress.

TAKE TIME TO DO IT RIGHT

How clothes fit has nothing to do with your height or weight. Clothes can be adjusted to any figure. But, as in Nancy's case, you may need time and patience to find exactly what you want. Among the vast choices available today, there are clothes to fit every body type. Some stores and manufacturers specialise in garments for very small women (yes, there is a size 4), while others cater to tall women or to large sizes (18 to 22). If you have special needs but don't know where to find them, ask at your favourite boutique or department store, or write to a fashion magazine for help. But never give in to the feeling that nothing better can be found, or that you are so tired (after a day of shopping) that second-best 'will do.'What you want is out there. Just don't get discouraged.

When you're in a shop trying on clothes, make sure you have an unobstructed three-way view of yourself in the mirror. If the fitting room doesn't have a three-way mirror, use your hand mirror to look at the back of the garment. There should be no pleats and pulls anywhere. Look at yourself from the side, too. You'll be surprised to see how many styles that look good front and back look less so sideways – perhaps revealing more stomach than you thought you had.

Once you have checked out front, back, and sides, look carefully at the following details.

Shoulders

For a set-in sleeve, the shoulder seam should be on your natural shoulder line. If it is farther out, you may look like an American football player; if it is too far in, you will appear to have grown out of the garment.

Lapels

They must lie flat. If they buckle or bulge, it is a sign that the garment is too small.

These must not have pull where the sleeve is set into the jacket, and no horizontal pleats or dimples on the arm. A question I am asked often is: 'How long should a jacket sleeve be?' To find the right length for *you*, measure from the tip of your thumb 5 inches up. That is where the sleeve should end. Your shirt or blouse should extend 12mm to 18mm beyond it.

Vertical wrinkles mean that a garment is too large. Horizontal wrinkles show that it is too tight. This rule applies especially to trousers. Horizontal pleats in the crotch area indicate that the trousers are too snug.

I will discuss correct proportions and appropriate styles for various figure types in later chapters. However, here are a few important points to remember regarding fit:

1. Fitness and fit go together. What I mean is the better the shape of your body, the tighter the clothes you can wear.
2. A heavier person will look slimmer in slightly loose clothes.
3. To test how good a fit is, see how a garment moves with you: sit down in it, bend in it, and walk in it. A good fit should be rather smooth in all positions.
4. Consider whether you want to wear a garment under or over something else. A coat, obviously, has to be roomy enough to fit over a jacket. A sweater to be worn under a shirt or another sweater must not be too bulky.
5. Decide what shoes you will wear with the garment. Its length can of course be changed, but it is better to find the right length without having to bother with alterations.

ALTERATIONS

And this brings us to the question of alterations. To achieve a perfect fit, alterations are often necessary. (I hardly ever buy anything that I don't adjust somewhere; this should not be necessary for someone who is 5 feet 8 inches and wears a size 10, but it often is if I want something just right.) Alterations should be considered mainly for the following: to shorten a garment, to lengthen skirts, trousers, or sleeves; or to take in the waist (when this is done, the most you can take in without damaging the style is 38mm). When shortening a jacket, skirt, or trousers, have the new hem pinned completely first and then try the garment on again to see if it is the correct length and to check the proportions. For example, if you have a jacket shortened, be sure the pockets are not too close to the edge of the jacket.

Unless you are a very good seamstress, have alterations done by an expert. This is especially true of hems, for one that is badly done can spoil a garment. (A 100mm hem looks very ugly.) When letting out a hem or sleeves, make sure that the fabric will not retain crease marks from the earlier length. Velvet, synthetic knits, satin, silk, and sometimes even cotton tend to do this. With wool and gabardine, on the other hand, the marks are easily removed with pressing. If the alteration comes close to remaking the garment, I do advise against it, as it will affect the style and never look right.

So before thinking of styles, pay attention to the colours and the fit of what you wear. As I have said, colours should be complimentary to you. They should make you look alive and bring out your personality. And for a garment to be flattering, it has to be well-made and fit in a way that enhances your body.

2

Lingerie and its Appeal

What's more exciting than suspense! Think of unwrapping a gift. The best moment of all comes when you're wondering what's in the parcel as you carefully open it. Not that the object loses its attraction when you see it, but the suspense adds to its appeal. It's the same with a woman and underwear. Lingerie is the wrapping paper for her body. It increases her desirability and sex appeal.

Your partner is, of course, already attracted to you, otherwise he wouldn't be there. But the act of 'unwrapping' can certainly add to the stimulation of the evening (or day). And, as you may know, some people don't unwrap their presents all the way. It's often fun to keep something back. A little mystery works wonders. I truly believe that nudity does not add to sexual appeal but instead detracts from it. It detracts from the art of seduction. The underwear a woman is wearing, if it's sexy, will certainly increase the pleasure and degree of eroticism she and her partner feel.

Lingerie gives you the chance to look and be someone else for a special occasion. Change keeps life interesting. A garter belt, a special bra, a sexy pair of stockings can be a great boost to your love life. I'm not saying this just for the benefit of your partner, but also for you. After a number of years, life may have gone a little flat for

A matching bra and half-slip will make you feel well co-ordinated even when under your clothes

you too, and you may not always feel inspired. But wearing sexy soft, silky underwear will change your mood. Feeling naughty and provocative will give you back the excitement you've missed. Just imagine going out for dinner wearing a beautiful red bra and bikini panties. Besides the pleasant feeling of the soft fabric against your skin, your anticipation of what your lover will say when he sees you will make you more seductive. Don't feel apprehensive about your image. When you see the effect, you'll soon forget your worries.

A LOOK BACK

Underwear as we understand it did not come into existence until the later Middle Ages. Most underpinnings started as outerwear and then went underneath, usually because they became more functional. The most elementary of early garments for both sexes was the loincloth, a forerunner of what is known to us as briefs. The corset started as an outer garment as early as the twelfth century, but not until three centuries later did it become an undergarment used by both women and men to improve on nature by artificially shaping the body and influencing the look of fashion for many years.

Another original function of underwear was to protect outerwear – which could not be easily washed and was often made from elaborate and costly fabrics – from bodies that did not enjoy a daily bath. Undergarments were therefore made from cotton or linen, which was easy to wash.

By 1900 underwear was being made from silk, satin, and lace, and was becoming seductive and a fashion in itself. As such, it now had a name of its own – lingerie.

It took the form of negligees and peignoirs, corsets (the Gibson Girl S-shape corset of 1904), combinations, drawers, and petticoats.

Underwear followed and was adapted to the fashion trends of outerwear. In 1907 the French designer Paul Poiret banished the curved S-shape figure by bringing into fashion a more natural shape, and with it the brassiere was born. In 1913 came a new concept of the brassiere, when the American Mary Philips Jacobs (later known as Caresse Crosby) brought out a new soft, short model that separated the breasts.

By the way, the terminology used to describe underwear has undergone constant change. Lingerie became known as undies in the 1920s, and petticoats became petties. Brassiere was shortened to 'bra' in the 1930s. Drawers first became stepins, then pants or panties: only after 1950 were they called briefs.

The discovery of nylon by Du Pont in 1938 is the most important invention in the history of underwear. Its attractiveness and low cost allowed underwear to be less exclusive, less expensive, and therefore available to women of all classes.

Elastic fabrics began to affect corsetry in the early 1920s, when shop catalogues referred to 'corsets of porous elastic.' They were further improved by new machinery that came into use in the 1950s, when fully elasticised foundation garments were made and introduced to the popular market.

With the youth explosion of the 1960s, underwear took a dramatic turn. The miniskirt had a lot to do with the disappearance of the girdle, regarded for many years as a must for a good figure. Tights and pantyhose replaced stockings, and made garter belts and girdles unnecessary. Underwear was losing its attraction. More and more women wore only a bra and tights or pantyhose.

The see-through fashions that appeared in the 1960s and Rudi Gernreich's no-bra bra, introduced in 1963, minimised the concept of underwear even further. The moulded seamless flesh-colour concept took over. Women now wore underwear that was nearly invisible and so were they. This type of lingerie does not enhance any woman's sex appeal. It might be necessary under certain clothes, such as knits, but I am sure that every woman has clothes in her wardrobe that will allow for a more exciting image than the flesh-colour look. Fortunately for us, designers are now giving us many choices in seductive looks.

Lingerie is a good way to be more seductive. Before you buy new lingerie, however, think about your assets. Look at yourself again, asking these questions:

About your BUST	• Is it small, medium, or large? Does it have a cleavage? Is it placed high or low? Is it pointed or round?
About your STOMACH	• Is it flat? Is it firm? Is it slightly protruding? Is it too big?
About your HIPS	• Are they narrow?

Are they in proportion with my shoulders?
Are they wide?

About your DERRIÈRE
- Is it the right size in proportion with my body?
Is it flat?
Is it big?

About your THIGHS
- Are they slim?
Are they flabby?
Are they heavy?

About your LEGS
- Are they long?
Are they short?
To analyse your legs, measure your torso from the shoulders to the top of the legs and then measure your legs. If the torso is much longer, your legs are short; if torso and legs are the same, your proportions are just right. But if your legs are longer, you are in fashion. For years now, long legs have been a great plus; and as I said before they are regarded as sexy.

CO-ORDINATING YOUR LINGERIE WARDROBE

No, we aren't going shopping yet. This time it's not yourself I ask you to look at, but at the underwear you now own. Start by taking all your lingerie out of your drawers and closets (make sure that none of it is in the laundry). Eliminate the items you wouldn't want to be seen in. Ask yourself why you bought them in the first place. If the flesh-colour bra was to go under your beige sweater, think back to when you bought it. Are you sure that there wasn't a more attractive model, maybe with more lace or a better cut? And what about the slip to wear under your knitted dress; couldn't you have found one that makes you look less like a sausage? With the choice of styles on the market today, we have no excuse for buying under-wear that is practical but not attractive.

After the first weeding out, you should be left with items you like and those you need for certain outfits.

Maybe some of the items you have kept are not exactly favourites, but you feel that you couldn't afford nicer versions. This brings us to the question of quantity. Do you really need fourteen bras and twenty pairs of panties? Most women wear four or five bras con-stantly; the others just lie in the drawer.

Think carefully about what you need before you buy. That way you can have five really good bras instead of ten or more mediocre ones. Maybe you hesitate to throw out panties because you do your laundry once every two weeks. You can solve this problem by washing your panties when you shower or bathe.

Then you will always have clean ones, you won't need so many, and you can buy more expensive styles. (This rule applies to every other item, too; buy less and you can afford to splurge.)

When co-ordinating what you need, coordinate the colours as well. The new shades in lingerie permit us to omit pinks and baby blues if we choose. Colours like burgundy, navy, chocolate brown, black, red, champagne, rose, and lavender allow us to select the most becoming and the most sexy colours, like black and red. (A study of men's reaction to colours showed that black is regarded as the most exciting, with red a close second.) Beige and flesh colours are not becoming because there is not enough contrast with the skin. Beige should be worn only when outer garments require it; for example, under a white blouse beige is less visible than white.

Co-ordinating your underwear is as important as co-ordinating your outer garments.

Pay the same attention to it.

Important points to remember: When buying a bra, do get the matching panties right away. Better yet, get two pairs, as they wear out faster than bras.

NOTE

If you like to wear floral panties for which no matching bra is made, pick one of the colours (preferably the most prominent) and buy a bra in that colour so the two items will look like a set.

If you can't find a bra to match your slip or panty, try matching the colour of the lace, which is often different from the colour of the fabric. For instance, if you have a mauve slip with black lace and can't find the same mauve in a bra or panty, buy them in black.

Now that you know your assets, are prepared to buy fewer but better things, and are aware of the colours you need, you are ready to shop.

ABOUT SHOPPING

Whenever you have an hour to spare, go into a shop and look at what is being offered. You don't always have to buy, but you will know what is fashionable. Feel the materials and consider how the new colours this season would look on you. Imagine how those sexy styles would make you feel. If you find something interesting, take it to the fitting room and try it on. ALWAYS TRY ON. You may be sure of your size, but a particular model might be all wrong for your figure. (This applies even to panties, which unfortunately most women don't try on.) I know it's frustrating to see something you like and not have the time to try it on. But don't take the risk. You might come home with an item that doesn't suit you. If you live in a town where it is difficult to find some of the items I discuss in this chapter, take a look at fashion magazines or other publications for women. Many have ads for underwear. You can probably find what you're looking for through mail-order houses.

Now let's look at the items that are available and consider what they can do for us.

BRAS

The idea of improving or supporting the breasts goes back a long way. Greek women wore a kind of band around the chest. It served its purpose but did not flatter the bustline. When the corset came, engulfing the whole figure, breasts looked sexy and provocative but women were not always comfortable. Today we're lucky because we can look sexy and be comfortable at the same time. In choosing a bra for:

A VERY SMALL BUST

TO MAKE IT LOOK BIGGER:

- A bra with pre-shaped cups (which is formed to look like a well-shaped bust).

- A slightly padded bra, the type that is padded all over. It feels like several layers of material without any rubber inside.
- A bra that is padded only on the lower part of the cup. The padding is like a small pillow supporting the breasts.
- A bra with an underwire. This always helps to push the breasts up and gives them a fuller look.

SHOWING CLEAVAGE.

With a very small bust it is difficult, if not impossible, to create a cleavage. However, you can turn this into an advantage by not wearing a bra and having a decolletage down to your waist (if you are brave enough.) It will look sexy and you will arouse the curiosity of everyone who sees you.

A SMALL BUST

TO MAKE IT LOOK BIGGER:

- An underwire bra will do for this type of bust what a padded bra does for a very small bust. It will give support and push it up enough to give a fuller look.
- A push-up bra. Remember the one Warner brought out in 1969? It was sexy, exposing

part of the breasts and at the same time giving an illusion of volume. The straps must be on the outside of the cup to create a fuller look by really lifting the breasts.

• A bra with moulded cups, if you want your bust to look round but not pointy. (If you want a pointed look buy bras with seams and darts in the cups.)

NOTE | *A word of caution:* If you want your bust to look bigger or more seductive, stay away from the soft no-bra looks. The moulded ones give the same general effects as the no-bra look, but they will make your look sexier

SHOWING A CLEAVAGE:

• A push-up bra that pushes the breasts both up and together gives the best effect.
• A demi-bra is another style for a provocative look. It leaves the upper part of the breasts exposed, plus showing a cleavage.

A MEDIUM-SIZE BUST

TO MAKE IT LOOK BIGGER:

• An underwire bra will push up the breasts giving a fuller look.
• A push-up style – again, be sure the straps are on the outside.

• A no-bra can be worn best by this size. It gives a very natural, full look and can be very sexy under knits. Often, however, the nipples can be seen through the soft material. If you don't want this effect, put plasters over the nipples.

SHOWING A CLEAVAGE:

• A push-up bra that is cut away in the middle, exposing the breasts. If you have a

natural cleavage and want to show it, don't wear bras with moulded full cups; instead wear lacy ones open at the middle.

• If you want to wear a plunging neckline without showing your cleavage, choose a bra with cups far apart and connected by only a small piece of elastic. It will separate the breasts and allow you to be sexy without being obvious.

A BIG BUST

TO MAKE IT LOOK SMALLER:
- A minimiser bra. This type of bra will reduce the breasts up to one size. It does this by pulling the breasts apart rather than pushing them together.
- A bra with round cups, not pointed ones. The pointed type adds volume to a large bust.
- An underwire bra with moulded round cups. It separates the breasts and gives a youthful look.

• A bra that does not pull the breasts up too high. To avoid this be sure the straps are in the middle of the cup, over the nipple.

TO REDUCE CLEAVAGE:
• A bra that has space between the cups to separate them.

NOTE The proper way to try on a bra, whatever size you are, is to close it and then bend forward and down. This will place your breasts well into the cups.

TEDDIES

A teddy is the top of a full slip plus a panty, all in one.

It can be worn with or without a bra under it; there are also models with built-in bras. A teddy fastens at the crotch with snaps or hooks. It may be made of satin or silk with lace trimming. You can also find it in a stretch nylon, like a bodystocking, and it fits very snugly around the body.

When made from a fabric like silk or satin, a teddy can be worn under a lined dress or skirt where no slip is needed. If you want to wear one under pants, the stretch type is better. When buying a teddy make sure that it is long enough in the torso to avoid discomfort. When trying on, sit down in it to be certain that it doesn't cut into you between the legs.

This garment is a charming alternative to bras and panties. It looks very feminine and seductive.

CAMISOLES

A camisole is like the top part of a teddy, extending a few inches below the waist. You can buy it as a separate item but a better alternative is to buy the matching panties; a matching half-slip will complete the set.

A camisole, like a teddy, looks good under a transparent blouse, or under a blouse that you leave open. It is even appropriate for an evening look when worn with a suit or under jackets. You can also wear it with a pair of jeans when you are at home; it will not look dressed up, but more seductive and feminine than if you were wearing a shirt or sweater.

I must point out here that this item of underwear looks best when worn without a bra. A bra often makes a camisole look messy because it's a different shape and adds a second set of straps. If, however, you wish to wear it anyway, make sure that the camisole covers your bra well. A style cut straight across the top is best.

CORSETS

The first corsets were made from wood, bone, and iron. Warner Brothers even made one that claimed to be rustproof. Today, fortunately, they are made from stretch materials or with supports that are comfortable. They are available strapless for small busts and with straps for bigger sizes. The garter straps are detachable so that the corset can be worn with or without stockings.

A corset makes us think of the French cancan. It is not something that we would wear in our daily life, but it is still with us, reserved for special events and people in our lives. What I'm thinking about is your love life. Just try to imagine the effect it might have on that special partner. You could wear a corset under a loose dress, for example, or under a lounging outfit. You could also wear it just with a skirt, showing the top of the corset. In the past this was often the fashion because of the prettiness of the styles. It will give a milkmaid image, which has always been very sexy.

Any figure type can wear a corset, from a very small size to a large one. Don't forget that the original purpose of this garment was to correct and shape figures, so even if you are a size 20 and 38-D cup, you can look sexy in a corset. It will hide any imperfections, like a little stomach or heavy hips, since it covers and holds you from your armpits down to the tops of your legs.

BODYSTOCKINGS

If you're not game enough for a corset, try a bodystocking for a start. Of course bodystockings have many uses other than seducing someone – for exercise, to keep you warm in winter, to complete a skirt, or even to replace a swimsuit. But to show and mould your body in a sexy way consider the type that covers you completely, from your neck to and including your toes. This can also be found with a deep V-neck décolletage. In a stretch lace and a dark colour it will be most effective.

Another style covers the torso, leaving the legs bare. This type too may be cut low in the front or back and is very appropriate when worn with a skirt for dancing. If you don't go dancing, wear it with jeans or trousers, or simply by itself (at home, of course). Make sure that you have the *right size*. If it is too small, it will flatten your bust or mould you to a point that shows the slightest bulge. If it is too large, it won't show off your body.

A lot of people believe that the bodystocking is a modern invention. Not so. The first type of bodystocking was made in the late nineteenth century and was called a union suit. It was so called because it united several garments in one, covering men and women from neck to ankle. It was worn not only by the latter-day frontiersman for warmth but also by the meticulous Edwardian to protect the outer garments from touching the body.

PANTIES

For Small Hips, Slim Thighs

This body type will look good in any sort of briefs. Obviously, the very skimpy styles, like G-strings or the type held together at the side with a bow or ring, are the sexiest (Illustration No. 1). Under trousers, however, they might show a mark or line where you don't want one, so a type extending up to the waist would be more practical.

Medium-Size Hips and Thighs

If your thighs are not as slim as you would like them to be, always choose a style that is cut high on the outside, exposing part of your hip (Illustration No. 2). This will make your legs appear longer and slimmer (and sexier). Stay away from boy-leg cuts; they are not only unbecoming but they make your legs seem larger than they really are. Also good for this figure is the type with a wide elastic lace band on top, extending to the middle of the stomach. Under trousers, choose a style that comes up to the waist (Illustration No. 3).

Big Hips, Heavy Thighs

If your hips are large and you are looking for a sexy panty, consider culottes, slit up the sides (Illustration No. 4). These are panties made like a little skirt. To look attractive, the leg part must not extend more than two inches over the top of your thigh. The advantage of the slit at the side is that it gives room as well as flare to the panty without revealing too much of the leg. (For this type of figure a high cut on the outside is not good, because it will expose what you don't want to show.)

Culotte panties can be worn only under a full skirt, not under a straight one or trousers. For trousers or a straight skirt choose either a pair of pantyhose that have a panty part like Underalls, or a brief that goes from your waist to the top of your legs, making a smooth line. Should you need more support, wear a brief made from elastic tricot. And if still more control is necessary, wear a panty girdle with longer legs, made from elastic tricot. To make this type of garment more attractive and sexy, buy it in black instead of white or a flesh colour. The darker colour will also make you look slimmer.

2

3

1

5

4

Bulging Stomach or Derrière

In this case a bikini or brief would be a disaster. Since this style does not extend to the waist, it will cut into the flesh, creating a spare tire. The best solution is an elastic panty that will give you a smooth line from waist to thigh. It can be sexy in a dark colour – burgundy, black, or brown – and in a fine fabric with a little sheen and pretty lace trim.

Flat Derrière

Many women are unhappy that they don't have a curvier bottom, but a flat one is easier to cope with than a big one! Unless you need a waist-high style for a particular outer garment, avoid this type, as it will make you look flatter. The panty should stop just above the curve of the bottom (Illustration No. 5). Select lace fabrics to add volume, or at least ample lace trimmings and frills. Buy panties slightly bigger than you need; the extra room will create the illusion of more.

Remember: Whatever style panties you wear, be sure to get them big enough. Asking for a size 10 may make you feel better than asking for a size 12, but most of the time the bigger size will be more flattering to your figure. Nothing looks worse than the spare tire created by elastic cutting into the flesh. This applies even to a very slim woman. **NOTE**

GARTER BELTS AND STOCKINGS

Before pantyhose were introduced, every woman wore either a girdle with garter straps or a garter belt. Today garter belts are reserved for a sensual look. If you discarded yours when pantyhose came in, it will be a pleasant change to buy a new one for a different, more sexy, image.

For a very slim figure the narrow type, which is essentially an elastic band around the waist with four garter straps, is the best.

For a more voluptuous figure choose the type made like a little skirt, extending halfway down over the stomach.

There are also panties with garter straps attached, which are good for all figures, but especially for a bigger-size woman. It will give the garter effect, without exposing too much.

To complete the seductive look of a garter belt, wear stockings of the same colour. If, however, black or red stockings are not appropriate with your dress, try stockings with seams up the back or with designs – like a few black squares or dots. Even net stockings can be fun with the right dress and certainly make for a sexy image.

The purpose of stockings with seams or designs is to draw attention to your legs. A sexy leg is always a welcome and intriguing sight, even for the most conservative men.

You might wonder whether pantyhose are sexy. I did quite a bit of research, asking different men how they felt about pantyhose, and their answers were all negative. In fact, more than one of them said, 'Pantyhose are the worst thing ever invented.' When I asked why, the reason men gave was that pantyhose wrap a woman up, making her look unavailable, and untouchable – they don't extend an invitation. When you think about it for a moment, you'll see the truth of this impression. So if you want to seduce someone, stockings and a garter belt will be more helpful.

These, of course, should always be worn with high-heeled shoes even when you're not wearing a dress.

SLIPS

Years ago, a woman always wore a slip or petticoat. Fashion changed this, first by lining skirts and dresses and then by putting us into trousers for many years. With the return of the dress (and the disappearance of linings, except in very expensive clothes), the slip has made a comeback. Unfortunately many women wear the wrong type, ruining the look of their outer clothes. The French call a slip a *fond de robe*, meaning a foundation for a dress. Certainly most dresses look better when they are supported by an undergarment. It makes the fabric fall better and keeps it from clinging to you in the wrong places. But if a slip is to do this job well it has to resemble the outer garment in shape and colour as closely as possible. Don't wear a white slip under a dark skirt or dress. Don't wear a full slip under a straight skirt; the extra fabric will look lumpy. Watch out, too, for a slip that is too long. (The French claim that when a woman's slip is showing she is looking for a husband – that might be so in France, but it won't do much for your image.) It's best to have your slip about an inch shorter than your skirt, but not more, especially if your dress is made of a thin or somewhat transparent material. If the slip is much shorter, there will be a visible gap, and the bottom of the dress will curve inward.

What type of slip to select depends on your figure – for a slim figure a bra and half slip are good. A camisole with a half-slip will be pretty, too.

For a larger or large figure, a full-length slip is best. It will not create bulges or interruptions and the line under a dress will be more uniform. To make this look more seductive, a slip with a built-in bra gives a cleaner, sexier look.

For those women who do not wear a slip, it might be of interest to know that wearing a slip will make your clothes last much longer. Remember that in the early days underwear was worn to protect the outer garments.

Any of the items I have discussed in this chapter can be found in various qualities, from a low-grade cotton to silk, satin, and laces, or shiny stretchy tricots. Whichever style is best for your figure, buy it in the prettiest variation you can find. Lace trims always add a softer feeling. A certain sheen or glitter can also make a difference in the appearance of an otherwise plain bra. Keep in mind that it should look pretty on you, as pretty as possible, as becoming as possible. This will automatically make you more appealing. You should never feel that you don't want to be seen in what you are wearing.

Has it ever happened to you that your underwear prevented you from enjoying an adventure? It did to me – only once, but I have never forgotten it and I have regretted it ever since.

The Italians have a proverb that will stand you in good stead:

ONE SHOULD ALWAYS BE DRESSED TO MAKE LOVE OR TO DIE.

3

Daytime Dresses – Alluring and Feminine

Would you believe that despite all those tight, tight jeans, men still find a woman most alluring in a dress? This might surprise you if you belong to the generation of young women who seem to have been born in trousers and only recently started to wear dresses. But men like to see a woman's legs. And their fantasies are further inspired by the way a dress moves with the wearer.

A feminine dress is one that flows around your body, follows each move you make, and clings here and there. How much it should flow and how much it should cling depends on how sexy you want to be. At this point you're probably picturing chiffon blowing in the wind. But to be seductive, a dress does not have to be chiffon or silk; the same effect can be achieved even with a cotton shirtwaist style.

HOW TO CHOOSE AN APPROPRIATE DRESS

The sign of a well-dressed woman has always been, and still is, to be appropriately dressed at all times. Your clothes should be suited to the time, the place, and the occasion. Wouldn't you wear a different outfit for a lunch than for a dinner party? Since a dress is the most versatile of garments, choosing the right one is particularly difficult. A dress can be joyful, sad, or threatening. Some dresses are mysterious; others say, 'I'm available.'

When you need a dress for a specific occasion, don't go to a shop thinking: 'Let me see what they have.' Do your homework first. Consider the purpose of the dress. Let's say that you're invited to an elegant dinner. You will need a style that is more outstanding, more daring than something you would wear during the day – perhaps a strapless dress or a low-cut dress with a jacket. Your next consideration is how many other dresses of this type you own. If you already possess several, you can choose a style that is fairly elaborate in design and colour. But if this is to be your only one, and you plan on wearing it on other similar occasions, you will want to buy something simple in design and quiet in colour. Its appearance can be changed with accessories – different jewellery, scarves, belts, or shoes – and no one will ever say: 'There she is in that pink number again.'

Now let's consider a different occasion – a dinner with business associates (yours or your partner's). You should choose a dress that you can also wear later on. You would not want a sporty style with stitching everywhere, but rather a classic design in a soft material. Here the type of fabric is really more important than the style. You could consider a shirtwaist dress in a fine wool, which, when worn with open-toed shoes and dressy jewellery – long earrings, or several bracelets, or an evening pin on the collar, or a string of pearls – would be appropriate.

NOTE	When buying a dress that you will wear mostly when sitting, such as at dinner or the theatre, or even behind a desk, make sure that the top is flattering to your face. Don't wear styles that have all the design and interest in the skirt.

CASUAL OR DRESSY?

In the days of our grandmothers, there were definite guidelines about what type of dress to wear for a specific occasion. If you read fiction set at the turn of the century, you may run across day dresses (or even morning dresses), carriage dresses, riding dresses, dresses for receiving callers, and so on. In our day the distinctions have been narrowed to two: casual and formal. But the reality is not so simple.

I have the feeling that when people don't really know how to define an occasion, or don't know how to dictate dress, they fall back on: 'Oh, you know, just casual.' Since this word has no exact definition, you may see party-goers in everything from jeans and a sweatshirt to a trousers suit with a satin blouse.

'Casual' means attire that is comfortable, not contrived, a look that does not say 'dressed up.' It does not mean sloppy, nonchalant, or unattractive. You can be casual in a good pair of trousers, a silk blouse, and a leather jacket, or in a cotton dress with sandals and a straw hat.

Since the definitions of 'casual' vary so much, you may want to call your host or hostess to get an idea of what to wear. There is no reason to feel embarrassed about doing so; it's a lot better than arriving in a T-shirt and denim skirt when everybody else is dressed in their Sunday best. **NOTE**

KEEP IT SIMPLE

Simplicity is as much a sign of a well-dressed woman as appropriateness. It even has an added value: it spells elegance. Most women, while admiring an elegant look, are totally lost when it comes to achieving it themselves. But it's not difficult. Three-quarters of looking elegant is simplicity. But looking elegant is not the only advantages of simplicity, especially in a dress. There are several extremely practical reasons too:

- The look of a simple dress can easily be changed with accessories.
- You will not get bored with a simple style as quickly as you will with an unusual one.
- A simple dress is versatile, for it can be worn on many different types of occasions.

These advantages are also reasons why you shouldn't be too worried about the latest fashion. Fashion changes so quickly that very few women can follow it to the letter. Simple, conservative styles are always in fashion. The best statement I have ever heard on this subject came from a woman who answered the question if she was fashionable this way: 'No–how could I be a different person every six months?'

Whatever style of dress you choose, there are two important things that will influence how it looks. One is length and the other is shoes.

SKIRT LENGTH

In the last chapter I wrote that poor colour co-ordination is the commonest mistake women make in dressing. Skirt length, whether in a dress or a separate, is the second – and one reason why a lot of women don't look as good as they could. You have probably heard or read that the most becoming length for women is between two and three inches below the knee. Fashion magazines and books constantly repeat this message, but it doesn't seem to penetrate – a lot of women wear their skirts too long. A skirt that's too long is unbecoming to everyone, especially a short woman. It makes her look as if she's standing in a hole, because her legs are not visible enough. Legs are an important part of being attractive.

I have always wondered why some short women wear their skirts so long. I got one explanation from a young woman who was five feet tall. Her skirt was made from a lovely beige material, buttoned down the front, but it reached almost to her feet. I looked at her in amazement and, since she was not a customer of mine, I tried to figure out a tactful way to suggest a shorter length. First I complimented her on the skirt itself; then I expressed regret at not seeing more of her legs. She answered, 'Oh, I wouldn't cut this lovely fabric. I paid forty-one pounds for this skirt.' I made one more attempt by saying that it would look even better if it were shorter, but she repeated that the fabric was too good to be cut. I guess she was afraid of losing fourteen pounds! This, by the way, is a typical example of a garment wearing the person and not the person the garment. Don't ever forget that clothes are there for you, not you for them.

Many of my clients ask, 'What is the right length today?' As we all know, the length featured at any given time jumps up and down like a yoyo. Don't worry about 'today's length.' The best length is one that suits you, the length that makes YOUR legs look good. I would agree with the standard advice by saying that the best, most flattering length for ninety-five percent of all women is just below the knee. For a SHORT WOMAN, it would be about an inch below the knee, and for a TALLER WOMAN two inches or more.

You can also go by the curve of your calf; a skirt should hit the leg where the curve starts. The worst length is midcalf.

To find the best length for *you,* you must take the trouble to try your clothes on and look at them. To ascertain how a skirt would look if it were shorter, turn the waistband over once, twice, or more. With a dress, use a belt to pull the dress up to a length which you think suits you. If a skirt is too short, take the hem down and then go through the above procedure. Keep in mind that an inch or two can make all the difference.

Before sewing a hem, pin it all around first and then try it on with the shoes you will wear. A skirt will look longer in flat shoes than in high heels.	**NOTE**

The reason you should look at each garment individually is because the right length can be affected by cut, the weight of the fabric, and even colour. A straight skirt in a dark, heavy material can be shorter than a light, full skirt, which needs a bit more length so you won't look like a little girl.

SHOES

A marvellous dress can be spoiled by shoes that don't fit its style or look old-fashioned. If you're wearing a flowing jersey wrap-around, for instance, a pair of clunky shoes will ruin the effect. On the other hand, an old dress can be brought up-to-date and made to look chic with shoes in the latest style. Why? Most people (men included) are very aware of the latest fashion trends when it comes to shoes. I certainly have never met a woman who was in doubt as to what shoes are stylish, even though she might have been unsure about clothes. (For more details on shoes, see Chapter 11.)

THE DIFFERENT STYLES OF DRESS

The Shirtwaist Dress

This is one of the most conservative of all dresses. It does change its style slightly depending on fashion trends, but it always has a collar, a buttoned front (at least to the waist), and sleeves. It is good for all figures. A SLIM WOMAN can wear a shirtwaist dress with a belt and a full (or straight) skirt; a HEAVIER WOMAN can wear it with a straight skirt and no belt. It is a very slimming look.

The shirtwaist is one of the most useful dresses you can own because it is appropriate for many occasions. It looks well in any fabric – cotton, silk, wool, poplin, or jersey – and is stunning in gold or silver lamé. Which material you choose depends on where you want to wear it. Be careful, however, how you wear it.

A customer of mine came to me with a shirtwaist dress that she had just bought but which her husband disliked. 'He can't say why, he just doesn't like it.' I asked her to put it on. She buttoned it up to the top, fastened the sleeves neatly at the wrist, and buckled the belt loosely around her waist. Result: no shape and no statement. I asked her to open the top three buttons, roll the sleeves halfway up her lower arm, and pull the belt in to show that she had a waist. The look was so different that her husband didn't even realise it was the same dress.

NOTE | When you decide how far a dress or blouse can be unbuttoned, don't look down at yourself. You will see a lot more than anyone else looking at you. To see what others see, look straight into the mirror and then decide.

44

*The classic
shirtwaist,
becoming to
most figure types.*

The Long-Waisted Dress

This style is good for a SHORT PERSON only if the torso does not reach lower than the hip bone. Otherwise, it will make her look shorter. But it is becoming for a SLIM WOMAN 5 feet 6 inches to 5 feet 8 inches tall. It is also good for a HEAVY WOMAN. The long torso will make her appear slimmer, with the pleats or softness of the skirt adding the movement needed for a sensuous look.

The Wraparound Dress

The wraparound dress made in pretty, soft materials, is easy to wear, and feminine: But there is no doubt that the style looks best on a SLIM WOMAN (although any height can wear it). On a HEAVY WOMAN the opening does not stay in place well, making the wearer feel awkward.

Never buy a dress in which you don't feel at ease. Feeling uncomfortable in a dress carries over into your behaviour and affects your self-confidence.

NOTE

The Chemise

The chemise is a basic style characterised mainly by an undefined waist. (The sack dress that appeared in 1957 was a version of this style.) Like the shirtwaist, the chemise is a constantly recurring look. If your figure is SLIM, you can easily wear this style with a wide leather belt (a narrow one will look lost). A HEAVY WOMAN will find that a straight look is best, without a belt.

The chemise is often made with a lot of fullness in the bodice, coming sometimes from the shoulders, sometimes from the bust. To avoid looking like a walking tent, make sure to pick a style where one point in the silhouette is touching your body, whether bust, waist, or hips. The rule applies to ALL FIGURE TYPES.

The T-Shirt Dress

A T-shirt dress can look great, but only on a woman with an excellent figure. In this case the style is less important than the fabric; T-shirt cotton is so soft and clinging that it really moulds the figure. Unless your figure can afford it, stay away from it. On the other hand, if you are firm and well shaped, you can wear a T-shirt dress no matter what your height.

The Empire Style

The empire style, first made popular by Empress Josephine in France, moves the waist up to just below the bust. The relatively shapeless fit below this point may be compensated for by a big décolletage, exposing the bosom and shoulders.

It is less popular today than it once was. But sun dresses are often made in this style, and so are maternity clothes. On the whole, this design does not do much for a woman's sensuality, although it is flattering for someone with a small bust.

The Princess Style

It is one of the most flattering cuts for ANY FIGURE TYPE,

Being fitted, without a seam at the waist, and with an A-line skirt, it will make the SMALL WOMAN look taller, a TALL WOMAN look elegant, and a HEAVY WOMAN appear slimmer.

Two-Piece Dressing

Two-piece dresses have become very popular. One of the reasons is that a two-piece dress can replace a suit in many cases. At the same time it gives a dressier look than a one-piece dress. It also hides figure flaws, such as a rounded stomach or some extra pounds on the hips. The two-piece dress can be very feminine if it has a flowing skirt that is partially hidden under the top. (The same full skirt in a one-piece dress might look unflattering.) It is a good style for most figure types except for the SMALL WOMAN; she will look better in a one-piece dress that does not cut her silhouette in half.

A word on wearing the two pieces separately. In most cases they belong together. Sometimes the top can be worn as a blouse with a different skirt. Usually, however, the skirt is difficult to interchange unless it is a print, which can be worn with a T-shirt or solid-colour blouse.

Another version of two-piece dressing, the dress with jacket, is very practical for several reasons. First of all, it is elegant-looking, since it is an ensemble. Secondly, it is appropriate for many occasions, from weddings to business meetings. And thirdly, you can make it work for both your professional life and your social life.

For example, a dress with a deep V-neck, spaghetti straps, or décolletage at the back will look perfectly demure during the day when covered up with a jacket. But if in the evening you remove the jacket it won't miss its effect.

The Sun Dress

Sun dresses are charming, cool, and comfortable. But they do belong in the sun, not at work or on big-city streets. The style of a sun dress is determined by the size of your bust, nothing else.

A SMALL or MEDIUM-BUSTED WOMAN who does not need a bra can wear any style – strapless, ruffled, or with small spaghetti strings. To add a little fullness, elasticised material that puckers and is made in strapless styles is very becoming. If your hips are small enough, you can wear this same fabric over your hips in a long-waisted style.

The SMALL or MEDIUM-BUSTED WOMAN who needs some support should wear a strapless bra under most sun dresses. Nothing is less aesthetic (or less sexy) than underwear when it's supposed to be invisible, so make sure your bra doesn't show.

A BIG-BUSTED WOMAN should not wear a dress that is so bare on the top that it will expose her shoulders and arms at the same time. A peasant-style bodice is a good alternative; if it is elasticised, you can pull it off your shoulders, making it both cooler and sexier. Another alternative is a sleeveless dress or one with cap sleeves.

IMPORTANT DETAILS

Necklines

For a neckline to be flattering, it should be either open or very high (like a turtleneck – more about this in Chapter 6). The shape does not depend on a woman's figure. Certain styles are unattractive on almost everyone, while others are universally flattering.

For the most unattractive style I would nominate the Peter Pan collar. Regardless of whether it has frills, lace, or bows, the image this style presents is either childish or old-maidish. The round neck (or jewel neck) also falls into this category. It is like the Peter Pan look, but without a collar. The trouble with this neckline is that it seems to cut your neck off at the worst place. It will look becoming only if it has a slit. A boat neck is an attractive alternative. It also comes up to the neck but the openness toward the shoulders makes it a more flattering design.

For the most attractive neckline, I would choose the V-neck. It is always around in some form or other. The beauty of it is that it suits every woman – small, tall, slim, or heavy. A SMALL-BUSTED WOMAN can wear a low V-neck. For the HEAVIER WOMAN it is a style that will make her look slimmer. It can be worn during the day or in the evening. It is also plain enough to change its look with accessories.

A big décolletage always looks better on a full-busted woman. A SMALL-BUSTED WOMAN is often too bony around the collar bones. A good solution for a woman like this, however, is a style that comes up to the neck in front but is cut low in the back. This cut draws attention away from the bust by exposing the back.

Skirts

When it comes to skirts, a slightly flowing or loose style is more feminine and youthful than a tight sheath. However, with a full skirt, the waist has to be pulled in to give the body some shape. The style of a skirt, contrary to that of a neckline, is influenced a lot by a woman's figure. A SLIM PERSON has a wide choice, but a HEAVIER WOMAN should limit herself to a moderate A-line, a dirndl style (slightly gathered in front and back), or a straight skirt. For her the most important detail is that the width of the hemline is not narrower than the hip measurement; if it is, the hips will look bigger.

Dresses with Ruffles

Ruffles stand for softness, innocence, romanticism, and luxury. With all these qualities, it's difficult to understand why they aren't more becoming. I've heard countless women say, 'I love ruffles, but not on me.'

For a SMALL WOMAN ruffles are not enhancing at all, not even on the sleeves or hem. They make her look smaller because they can easily be overpowering. A common style these days is the blouse with an enormous ruffled collar. This big collar tends to swallow up most wearers. Again it is a case of the garment wearing the person.

For a MEDIUM-TO-TALL WOMAN ruffles can look sexy around a V-neck, the wrists, or a fairly deep décolletage. On the hem of a skirt they look rather charming and soft.

If you have a very very SLIM FIGURE you can also wear a skirt made up of layers of ruffles.

Even if you have the figure for ruffles, however, you should still consider how comfortable you are in them. If you feel awkward, stay away from them for daywear. Keep them for your leisure wardrobe.

Do you get the impression that I don't like ruffles very much? You're right. Basically, I feel that more often than not they tend to hide the wearer. The exception is ruffles around the hem of a skirt, which do add movement and fluidity.

Short Versus Long Sleeves

A long, full sleeve is appropriate and flattering. For a SLIM WOMAN it gives an elegant touch, for a HEAVIER WOMAN it makes the arms appear slimmer. A long sleeve also looks more dressy. For example, a long-sleeved silk dress looks fabulous at the theatre, while the same dress with short sleeves would not look so appropriate.

Since long sleeves lead the eyes to your hands, pay attention to your manicure.

NOTE

Short sleeves are best left for sporty outfits. Some short-sleeved sweaters look very attractive, but wear them only if your arms qualify (bony elbows are not attractive) and the occasion is right.

The three-quarter length is not very flattering. A sleeve like this cuts your arm at an awkward place, and can easily look too short or like something you've grown out of, especially when it's tight. A fuller sleeve looks better. You might say, 'I roll up my sleeves or push them up to a three-quarter look – isn't that the same?' No, it's not. The extra fabric gives a casual, relaxed image that a three-quarter sleeve does not have.

SOME SPECIAL FABRICS

Knits

The knit dress in one form or another is never gone for long. It may be replaced for a while by jersey materials, but it always comes back. Since knits cling, your figure will determine the style and type of knit you can wear.

A SHORT SLIM WOMAN will look taller in a one-piece dress in a fine-to-medium knit. This should be straight, without a belt or other details, though it might have a turtleneck. (Caution: no heavy knits.)

A SMALL HEAVY WOMAN looks good in a two-piece dress in a fine knit. The skirt should be slightly flared. The top, which must not be longer than the top of the hip bone, should be loose and can be in a sweater style or buttoned like a jacket.

A MEDIUM SLIM WOMAN can wear knits in all forms and shapes. Be sure, though, the skirt is not too tight across the bottom.

A HEAVY WOMAN of MEDIUM HEIGHT should stick to a two-piece version made like a suit. Again, the knit must not be fanciful or heavy (nothing like a cable knit).

A TALL SLIM WOMAN can wear a one-piece knit in a fine rib, but she should break up her silhouette by a belt; otherwise she will look too thin. A two-piece serves to break up the silhouette, and here a TALL WOMAN is lucky, for she can afford to wear every type of knit, even those made from heavy yarn. She can carry the extra bulk through her height. Only this type of figure, by the way, looks well in big, bulky cardigans made from thick wool in many different colours.

A TALL HEAVY WOMAN should stick strictly to plain two-piece knits that resemble suits. This type of garment should not hug too closely anywhere. The jacket should fall straight, fitting loosely around the hips, and it should be long enough to cover half of the bottom. The skirt should be gently flared. When worn with a blouse under an open jacket, this type of dress can even replace a suit.

In fact, a two-piece knit dress or suit in the V-neck cardigan style can be worn well by ALL FIGURE TYPES. It has great versatility, for example during the day you can wear it buttoned up, or with a blouse under it or wear it in the evening without the blouse and add some pretty jewellery.

Wearing the right type of underwear is important at all times, but never more so than with knits. Since they hug the body closely, lingerie should be as smooth as possible. Wear a slip or petticoat without lace trimmings to keep the garment from clinging in the wrong places. Avoid lace bras, or bras with seams that show through. Also stay away from bikini-style panties. **NOTE**

Regardless of season, knits have a great advantage when it comes to travelling. With a knit dress, you never have to worry about wrinkles. You can take it out of your suitcase and put it on immediately. **NOTE**

YOUR OWN STYLE

The dresses I have talked about here are the classic, basic styles from which most other designs derive. The big difference in these silhouettes is not the design, but the shape. Each year or season fashion will favour one form, one look more than another in order to create a change. However, the latest preference of the designers does not mean that everything else is old-fashioned. When the short suit jackets came in again they were considered the latest styles, but the fashion magazines still showed designs with longer jackets. So your options are always there. You are the one who decides. Designers don't dictate, no matter what the critics say. They present you with various choices which you are free to accept or decline.

The style of dress that is best for you is determined by your height and figure. For most of us there are probably several options, but there is usually one that suits us best. Taking myself as an example, I can say that nothing becomes me more than a classic garment with open collar, lapels, and long sleeves. How dull, you may think. Not true. This basic look comes in dresses, suits, blouses, dressing gowns, and even beach robes. I can wear it in whatever colours and fabrics suit me, from wool tweed to white satin.

Once you have found the silhouette most becoming to you, stick to it and wear it in all the versions and types of garments you need. Don't worry about always looking the same. The different versions and colours are so numerous that you will have plenty of variety.

Wearing what suits you best, and only that, is called having your own style. Look at people you know or public personalities who you think are lucky enough to have their own image. If you analyse their appearance, you will see that all their clothes are of the same type and shape. (The late Jacqueline Onassis was an example.)

It isn't difficult to find your style if you stick with what suits you best. To test whether the dress you're wearing really is helping your image, listen when someone pays you a compliment. When he or she says, 'What a lovely blue dress,' take another look at yourself. The dress may be more visible than you. But if the compliment is more on the order of 'You look very nice,' that's what you want. Your dress should never be what people remember. They should only remember how good you looked.

4

The Suit and You

For many years now the skirted suit has been in the limelight. This is not because of fashion's whim but because the skirted suit carries an important message, one that says, 'I am a professional.' With all this attention, it has sometimes seemed as if the suit was a new invention. But of course this is not so. The suit has been around a long time, it was even fashionable in the nineteenth century when skirts were still worn to the floor.

Besides the suit's ability to project a professional image, it has other important qualities. It is one of the most comfortable, most becoming, most versatile items of apparel one can wear (probably the reason why men have been wearing them for so long).

A suit is comfortable because it makes you feel appropriately dressed. Also, you can adjust to temperature changes easily by wearing either a sweater or a blouse under it, or by simply removing your jacket if you feel warm.

A suit is becoming because everyone can wear it in one form or another. It is the garment that hides figure flaws best. Think of a large waist, a protruding stomach, a small bust, large hips – all are hidden by the jacket. Narrow or sloping shoulders are improved by the padding. (Nor are women the only ones hiding flaws; a man also camouflages a pot belly in a good suit.)

A suit is versatile because it is accepted for casual or formal wear, professional situations, social events, and for gala occasions like weddings. A suit will solve almost any fashion bind. Whenever you don't know what to wear, choosing a suit will be right ninety-nine percent of the time as long as the style and the fabric accommodate the occasion.

A suit is great for travelling, too, partly because it adjusts so well to climate changes. Suits help you avoid a lot of luggage, as you can change your look with different blouses and accessories. And wearing a suit while travelling is advantageous for looking properly dressed upon arrival, so this way you won't have to rush to your hotel to change before meeting your friends or business associates.

| **NOTE** | Never wear a solid dark colour during a flight. It picks up all sorts of fuzz, even the fluff from airline blankets. |

Keep in mind that the usefulness of a suit depends a lot on the fabric. A tweed suit, being a more sporty, casual day look is not as serviceable as the same style in gabardine, which is appropriate for any time of the day. Remember, too, that since a suit is so versatile and worn so often, it has to be of good quality. Only this way will you be assured of a good cut, a good fabric, and a good finish. If spending from £150 to £200 (somewhat less for summer) scares you, think of all the things a good suit can do for you, and all the places you can wear it. If you say that you can't afford it, I would advise you to reduce your wardrobe in order to have fewer but better clothes. You must realise that IT IS NOT IMPORTANT TO LOOK DIFFERENT EVERY DAY, BUT IT IS IMPORTANT TO LOOK GOOD EVERY DAY. The advantages of a good quality garment are:

- It lasts longer.
- It fits better.
- It looks better.
- It makes you feel better.

To get the maximum wear out of a suit, stay with conservative styles (like the ones shown in the pictures) in basic colours and fabrics.

Wool gabardine, or a mixture containing it, is a good year-round fabric for all but the hottest days.

For daytime wear the choice of blouses is endless. Do be sure, though, that the collar of the blouse does not conflict with the collar of the suit – for example, a blouse with a rounded collar and lapels worn in a jacket with a pointed collar and lapels.

Turtlenecks or other sweaters permit a more casual look that is still appropriate for the office.

A suit lends itself well to evening wear. For dinner or the theatre, a white silk or polyester blouse, plain or with lace trimmings, would be fitting. A beige lace blouse would also be very charming. Or, if you want to be more daring, wear a deep V-neck sweater. For a visit to a disco, wear just a camisole made from shiny material or a glittering fabric.

In the old days many women had evening suits, but today they are not useful unless you lead a rather formal social life. An evening suit would be made in silk or satin, perhaps with gold trim.

FLATTERING DETAILS FOR ALL FIGURES

When it comes to choosing the type of suit that becomes you most, proportion is the most important detail – the relationship between your height and/or weight and the style of the suit. The style of a suit depends mainly on (1) the length of the jacket; (2) the shoulders; (3) the lapels; and (4) the skirt. (Whether the jacket is loose or fitted influences the look, but less than the other details.) Your figure type therefore decides which style is best. As far as fashion is concerned, certain trends may become you more than others. But fortunately, on the merry-go-round of fashion we all get our turn. So if you have to wear longer jackets when short ones are in vogue, don't feel bad; the most important thing to remember is: 'Fashion is what suits you.'

Now let us see how details affect who can wear what.

Jacket Length

A SMALL SLIM WOMAN will look best in a fitted short jacket. If she is a BIT HEAVY, a slightly looser style is better, but it should still be on the short side, maybe two inches longer than that for a slimmer woman.

The SLIM WOMAN, 5 feet 6 inches, can choose any jacket length that pleases her. Fitted or loose, however, a style that can be worn with a belt will be more attractive.

A TALL SLIM WOMAN, 5 feet 8 inches and up, can also wear many styles, but again, a fitted or belted style will show her figure best. This figure type looks well in both long and short jackets, but short styles give a younger look. A TALL HEAVY WOMAN should wear a straight, fairly long jacket, but nothing longer than halfway over the bottom or it will make her look heavier.

If you have always preferred long jackets because you feel they hide your figure flaws, try one of these on, but fold under the hemline a few inches. Now look at yourself from the side. Doesn't it look better this way than with the additional bulk? If you insist on a long look, wear a three-quarter jacket; it will be slimming and cover more of you.

Shoulders

The type of sleeve and how it is set-in can make a big difference in the look of a suit. A set-in sleeve on the natural shoulder line is best for both the SMALL WOMAN and a HEAVY WOMAN. For the former, it will add an illusion of height and breadth; for the latter it gives a more controlled look. For a woman with sloping shoulders, the padding will replace what nature omitted. A raglan sleeve is good for a woman with broad shoulders, making them look less prominent.

Lapels and Collars

Narrow lapels and collars tapered to the waist create an illusion of length for a SMALL WOMAN, regardless of whether she is slim or heavy. The SLIM TALL WOMAN can afford to follow the fashion and wear any style she fancies, from very wide to very narrow. A broad-shouldered woman, whether slim or heavy, should avoid large lapels or collars; they emphasise breadth by leading the eyes to the shoulders.

Skirts

The most effective way to make a suit more feminine is the skirt. Given a jacket in a classic style, the skirt could make a suit more feminine if it is:

- a fuller A-line for a SLIM WOMAN of any height.
- moderate A-line for a HEAVIER WOMAN.
- gathered for a SLIM WOMAN.
- pleated for a SLIM WOMAN.
- designed with several pleats on one side for a SLIM WOMAN. (The same skirt is good for a HEAVY TALL WOMAN provided the pleats are closed halfway down the thigh.)
- made with inverted pleats at the bottom for a TALL WOMAN, SLIM or HEAVY.
- styled with a kick pleat in the middle of the front – open to the top of the thighs for a SLIM WOMAN, but not so high for a HEAVY WOMAN. This type of skirt is particularly good for the latter, as it adds flare without bulk.
- made with off-centre pleats at the front – good only for a SLIM TALL WOMAN, as this detail leads the eye toward the sides and draws attention to the hips.
- straight, with a pleat in the centre back, opening only on the lower part of the skirt. Good for ALL FIGURE TYPES.

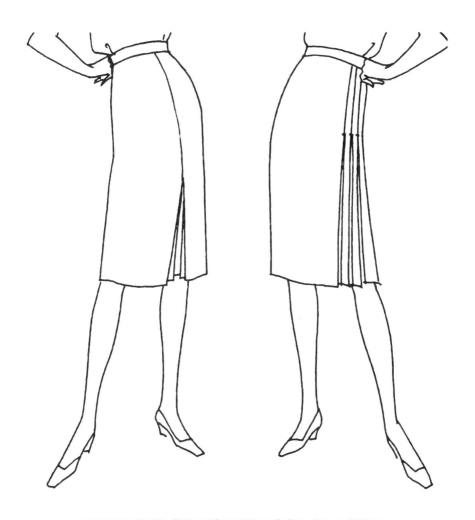

DETAILS TO CHANGE THE LOOK OF A SUIT

Sometimes we feel as though we'd like to discard suits. We want to look different. Here are details that can make our most favoured garment look and feel different.

- lapels in a different colour – for example, a royal-blue suit with black lapels.
- lapels made from a different fabric – for example, a black wool suit with black satin collar and cuffs.
- a jacket in a different colour from the skirt. This is becoming for a very tall person who wants to reduce height. It also helps a VERY HEAVY WOMAN draw attention away from her torso or hips – whichever is heavier.

Several types of suits convey a definite image and message. Following are the most important.

The Black Suit

A black suit can be one of the most useful pieces you own. Although some women feel that a black suit connotes dressing up for a special event, this is no longer true. You can now wear one anywhere, even to the office. It will give you authority. It is also elegant when lunching with friends or your partner. It can easily be changed to an evening look with a dressy blouse. Not only does black look good in any style and any fabric, but it is also very becoming for ANY FIGURE TYPE.

A White Suit

In the summer, or in a climate where white is appropriate most of the year, a white suit is good to own in addition to a black one. You can interchange the two quite easily. White also gives an impression of glamour or luxury without looking too dressy. And it makes its wearer look younger.

NOTE | Something to remember is that white must be of good quality. A white garment in a cheap fabric will make you look that way.

The Chanel Suit

I would say that, next to the classic styles that have been around a long time, the Chanel suit has been the most successful. Its success is due to its simplicity, and its suitability for any woman..

Double-Breasted Suits

A double-breasted suit is good only for a TALL SLIM WOMAN. And since this design tends to go out of style rather quickly, she might feel that the investment is too high. Remember also that this style does not look becoming when worn open.

Suits without Collars and Lapels

A jacket without a collar gives a quite different but very flattering look. On a SMALL WOMAN, SLIM or HEAVY, it elongates the torso, and can never be overpowering. It is good for a woman with a SHORT NECK, as it avoids a bunched-up look. It gives the TALL SLIM WOMAN a chance to wear elaborate blouses, with a large bow or big collar.

For a HEAVY WOMAN this style gives the illusion of length. She should be careful, however, that the jacket meets in front. I have seen jackets barely covering the bust; the space in the middle makes a person look bigger.

NOTE
An advantage of this style is that finding a blouse, sweater, or top to wear with it is easy since there is no conflict of collars.

Three-Piece Suits

If you want to look more feminine don't wear this style. A waistcoat can be sexy for at-home wear, but with a suit it will not enhance your female image.

The Pinstripe Suit

This, in any design, is the most unfeminine of all suits. Even though it has a skirt, it says from far away: 'Imitation man.' To look feminine, stay away from this fabric pattern.

Tweed Suits

A suit in tweed is a very useful addition to a wardrobe. It looks good for sporting events, work, and for travel. It is also easy to match with other skirts or jackets in a solid colour. Provided the tweed is in quiet shades and the material is not too thick, this suit can be worn by ALL FIGURE TYPES.

NOTE As most tweeds are a mixture of several colours, be careful when choosing a blouse. The most natural reaction is to match one of the colours in the suit. If your tweed contains dark brown and light beige, with burgundy accents, you might think that a burgundy blouse would be a good choice, but it isn't. A dark colour like this will make your outfit look drab. Instead choose one of the lighter shades.

Trouser Suits

When to wear a trouser suit is very much a matter of fashion and personal preference. There was a time when this style was not allowed in certain work situations or for certain occasions. But those barriers have now been obliterated.

Everyone likes a change from time to time. And the trouser suit is a very comfortable, casual approach to dressing that most women can wear. (The exception is the woman with very heavy thighs, who looks better in a skirt.) For travel and sporting events the trouser suit is ideal.

The Safari Suit

For sportwear this is one of the most becoming and youngest-look-ing styles you can find. It looks best when made with pants, and when the colour is khaki, beige, or white. (Colours like pink or rose are out.) Because of the many details – pockets, buttons, belts, and so on – this is a style for a FAIRLY TALL, SLIM WOMAN. On a small heavy person the details add bulk and overwhelm the figure.

INTERCHANGING SUIT JACKETS, SKIRTS, AND PANTS

Whether to wear the top of one suit with the bottom of another (or with a separate skirt or trousers) is a delicate matter. The most important thing to consider is the type of fabric. You can't wear poplin or a woolly material with a polyester fabric. The materials must be compatible in weight and type. Of course, style plays a part, too. A jacket without a collar or in a conservative style is easy to change around, but when it comes to intricate designs, it is more difficult. Some jackets say 'suit.' If you possess one of them don't interchange it with anything else.

NOTE | Whenever you are buying a suit and a third piece – whether skirt or pants – is available, buy it. It might be more expensive at the time, but the price of the third piece saves you from buying another suit. You will get twice the wear out of the suit. A jacket doesn't wear out as fast as a skirt or pants.

WHAT TO WEAR WITH A SUIT

A blouse that fits with the collar of a suit, that lies flat, that does not annoy you by bunching up is indeed difficult to find. I have heard endless complaints and have often been asked, 'How can I find the right blouse?'

My first advice is that you can find the right blouse only if you wear or take your suit along to the store when you're looking. It is still better if you buy at least one blouse when buying the suit. You will see whether the collar of the blouse is compatible with the suit style and collar.

To prevent a blouse from slipping out or bunching up, the material has to be soft and not a synthetic blend (which seems to have a mind of its own). Blouses and shirts with lapel-type collars are the commonest right now, but as an alternative, try a V-neck or cowl-neck blouse (especially for evening). The choice of sweaters is as vast as other tops, but to be really sure one will look well under your suit, try them on together.

You may be surprised when I tell you that T-shirts look very good with suits. (By T-shirt I mean a simple, solid-colour cotton T-shirt.) They give a nice clean look that is attractive but never messy or overpowering. You might think that a T-shirt is not appropriate for business, but consider how little of it is actually seen – just a small area in the middle of the jacket. It is cheaper than a blouse and it is easier to find the right colour since they come in so many shades. A T-shirt is also good for women with short necks, on whom two sets of collars can be uncomfortable and unattractive.

Camisoles in silky materials, glittering fabrics, or lace – perhaps elasticised – strapless or with small strings, are all very handy for changing a suit into an evening look. Don't worry about feeling naked, because chances are you won't be taking off your jacket.

72

5

Beautiful Coats

A coat is not A separate piece of clothing but part of your total outfit. It should pull a look together. In order to do so, the first requirement is that a coat be in the colour tones of your wardrobe, or at least complementary with them. For example, if your basic colours are navy and grey, you could consider a burgundy coat. The two most useful colours are black and beige. (Note that beige does not soil as quickly as many people think.) Both colours are good for many occasions, even in the evening.

Of course, how basic you have to be depends on how many coats you own. Most women I meet have one they wear all the time (plus one or two others from previous years). For an all-purpose coat you need to stay basic in style and colour. If you can afford a second and third one, your choice could be a coat strictly for evening wear, a tweed coat, or one that is part of an outfit.

Remember that a coat is an investment. It is also one of the most important pieces in your wardrobe. In cold or even cool weather, more people see you in your coat than in what you have on underneath. Many times you won't take your coat off from the time you leave home until you return, whether you are shopping, going to the movies, or taking a walk. Thus it often creates the first impression you make.

For a coat to look becoming it should not reveal what you're wearing underneath, except for a turtleneck. Your skirt should not show through a slit or because the coat is too short.

A Basic wool coat, suitable for most women. The colour white gives it a look of luxury.

If you will look around you'll notice that there are two lengths that dominate – too short and too long. What do you think when you see a woman wearing a coat that's too short?

- The coat must be a few years old.
- She doesn't have the money to buy a new coat.
- She isn't very fashion-conscious.
- She is negligent about her appearance.

Whichever one of these conclusions applies, one thing is certain: the result is not attractive.

On the other hand, a coat that's too long gives the impression of a garment walking down the street dragging along a person. It makes most women look shorter, and reduces a small woman to midget size. It also looks especially unattractive without boots.

What is the correct length? A coat should be one inch longer than your skirts. At that length you can wear it with boots as well as with a pump or evening shoe.

TYPES OF CLOTH COATS

Because there are so many coat styles from which to choose, and because the garment is such an important item, you need to be particularly careful when buying a coat. The main characteristic of a good-looking coat is a casual, loose feeling. It should not look constrained or buttoned up but rather relaxed and flowing, even when worn with a belt.

Wraparound Style

This is the coat that best conveys a casual message. Being ample and casual, it goes over any style dress or outfit, can be worn by day or night, looks attractive on ANY FIGURE TYPE, and is easy to wear.

NOTE	Make sure that the overlap is large enough so it really wraps your body. To increase the charm of this style, always turn up the collar.

Double-Breasted Style

The opposite of the wraparound coat is the constricted style. It looks well only on a SLIM TALL WOMAN. For a SMALL WOMAN it is too overpowering and. For a HEAVY WOMAN it adds weight.

Raglan-Sleeve Style

To camouflage very broad shoulders, this is a suitable look. However, if you have sloping or narrow shoulders, this cut will emphasise them.

Fitted Styles

Fitted coats are more difficult to wear than a loose coat – only a trim slim figure looks good in it. It also limits what can be worn underneath. Because this style hugs the body closely, the SMALL SLIM WOMAN can wear it best without looking constrained; she can actually look quite graceful in it. Although the tall person can wear a fitted coat this figure type would look better in a loose coat, where the belt will give the shape to the figure.

Loose Styles

There are many pretty styles that are worn without belts and that provide a flattering alternative for the HEAVY WOMAN. The most becoming cut is the one that flares out toward the hem, fitting around the upper part of the torso.

When made with a mandarin collar, buttoned down the front it is charming for a SMALL WOMAN too.

Coats with Hoods

A hood adds charm as well as keeping you warm and protecting your hair. A soft small band of fur around it is lovely. This style, however, would not do if you have only one coat. As an additional coat, it is good in tweed for a casual look or in black or dark wool for evening wear.

Duffel Coats

A duffel coat is warm and practical. If you have several coats, it brings a pleasant change to your wardrobe. Remember that it is not a suitable everyday look and only SLIM TALL WOMEN look well in it. Duffel coats are also more feminine with a hood.

Reversible Coats

Whenever we come across a reversible coat, we are delighted, thinking that the possibility of turning it inside out will give us a second coat. But if you've ever owned one, you know that it doesn't work that way. Usually it's worn on one side only. So think twice. The contrasting colour is limiting. (An exception is the coat with a mandarin collar or no collar, which is more practical.) If the coat does have contrasting lapels, it is not a good style for a SMALL WOMAN or a HEAVY WOMAN.

Trenchcoats

Did you know that this coat got its name from a similar style worn by British officers in the trenches during World War I? It has since become one of the most basic coats for both men and women. I think that its success comes from the fact that it is practical and suitable for many people and occasions. It is also made in a wide variety of fabrics.

The original design was double-breasted and belted, with epaulets, gun flaps, and a multitude of pockets. Since then this model has been modified in many ways. You can find it single-breasted, without the epaulets, or beltless.

To me, the original design is still the most attractive. It can be worn well by most figure types. If you are very small, however, choose a style that does not have epaulets and shoulder yokes. If you are on the larger side, wear a beltless style without epaulets, as they add bulk.

SOME SPECIAL FABRICS

Down Coats

Down coats come in all shapes and colours. For a heavy person, I would most certainly not recommend this style. I overheard a man say that his wife 'looked like a marshmallow' in hers. If you are tall and slim you might be lucky to find a style that will not make you look too bulky. Unfortunately, many short women are also wearing down. Their main concern is obviously warmth and comfort, and this they get. But if you are short or heavy and want down, at least have the coat shortened to fit you properly. This will cost money, but it is worth it; otherwise you will look as if the coat is wearing you.

Leather Coats

How good a leather coat looks depends on how much you can spend for it. The reason is that a cheap coat is made from inferior skins, which are very stiff. When a garment lacks suppleness, it will not move with your body. This applies as much to suede as to any other kind of leather. So unless you consider buying top quality, you'd be better off staying away from it.

If a leather coat or jacket has always been your dream, buy it in a conservative style – it's an investment that will have to last many years. As to style and fit, follow the same rules as those for cloth coats.

Raincoats

A raincoat has always been a necessary garment in everyone's wardrobe. In the 1960s, however, it became an important fashion item as well, even replacing the spring and fall coats that were once worn during those seasons.

Instead of being made only from gabardines and poplins, raincoats come in many different fabrics and colours, including black silk.

To me a raincoat is one of the most practical coats, provided you choose the right style. The trenchcoat as a raincoat is one example. What makes it attractive are all the details, such as epaulets, pockets, and belt.

Many of us still look for a raincoat that can be worn for many years, but since it has become a fashion item, I feel that a raincoat

should be changed every two years or so. The best colours are still beige and black. Remember that there are many different shades of beige. A very pale tone is not too practical. Not only does it soil quickly but the colour lacks definition. Try the darker beiges instead. Black has an added advantage in that you can wear it as an evening coat. Do not go for such bright shades as mauve, red, or royal blue. You will stand out and be remembered too much, as well

When buying an umbrella, think of the colour of your raincoat. I am not trying to be dull, but a blue umbrella with white flowers does not do anything for a black raincoat.

NOTE

as have trouble matching the colour with what you wear underneath. If your figure does not allow for elaborate details like multiple pockets and buttons, choose a style that is plainer, and make up for the lack of detail with a more interesting fabric. A shiny material, for instance, has a great deal of appeal.

SOME SPECIAL STYLES

Jackets

Since a jacket is a short version of a coat, many styles are made like the coats I've already discussed, and what I said about suitability still applies.

How many jackets you need depends on how often you wear pants and how many of your suit jackets you can wear with them. There is no doubt that pants look more youthful when worn with a jacket. And if your suit jackets look attractive with your jeans, you are not going to need many others.

For a SMALL WOMAN the so-called Eisenhower jacket is very becoming. A long-legged TALL WOMAN will also look well in this style. As a matter of fact, it will make those long legs look even longer, but then, she has many other styles from which to choose.

Capes

Capes keep appearing again and again, but are never accepted by a mass audience. They are not warm or very comfortable to wear. Can you see yourself traipsing home from the supermarket with two armloads of grocery bags while wearing a cape?

A cape is best in the evening and can be thrown over any outfit, long or short, winter or summer. For winter you could have one in a heavy material, maybe with a hood. For the summer use a lighter fabric, even an 'ethnic' cloth such as a South American print. Since the cape is a dramatic garment, the fabric can be bold as well.

Now, who can wear a cape? A TALL SLIM WOMAN. Not only should she have this figure, but she has to have a certain theatricality as well. You can't arrive unnoticed in a cape. So if you don't stand at least 5 feet 6 inches tall and feel game enough to carry it off, forget capes.

If some heavier women believe that a cape is advantageous because it fully covers their figure they're mistaken. In actuality it makes them look bigger.

FUR COATS

The controversy of wearing real fur has been with us now for many years, and the protest against women who still love the feel of real fur and the manufacturer who make fur garments, is still growing.

Recently a group of demonstrators invaded the Vogue offices in New York, chanting (quote) 'Fur shame. Compassion is the fashion. Don't buy fur, don't buy Vogue.' They were protesting Vogue's fur editorial and advertising.

It has become a very emotional issue and what a woman believes to be right in this matter, is a personal decision. Fortunately for those woman who feel that they don't want to wear a real mink coat, the textile industries has come up with a wonderful alternative – fake furs.

Since most type of furs have been recreated in the man-made version, the rules of suitability as far as fur is concerned, are the same for a fake mink, or fox as they are for the real thing.

Therefore, while reading the advice given here, please keep in mind that it applies to both, real as well as fake furs.

Choosing a Fur

Buying your first fur coat will probably be a difficult purchase. The price if real or fake makes it an investment that does not allow for errors. So before you even go to a store, think about the coat's purpose and your lifestyle. Do you want to wear the coat at all times, is it to keep you warm when you go skiing, or is it only for evening wear? Being specific will help you decide not only the style but also the kind of fur you buy.

Mink

If you want to wear a fur coat around the clock and have it go over everything in your wardrobe, you will need a durable but not flashy fur of short to medium hair, like mink. Mink is the top-selling fur, and no wonder. It is warm, lightweight, and long-wearing. It can be worn for casual or dressy events. It is slimming and flattering for most figure types.

The best shades are dark or medium brown.

Black ranch mink, is less flattering to most women than a deep brown.

Other everyday furs, which come in a variety of colours, are raccoon, opossum, mole, skunk, nutria, muskrat, and sheared beaver.

Lamb

Lamb is a fur that comes in different weights. The finest, broadtail, is also known as Swakara. It is so soft that it drapes like cloth. It is not very warm, but it is an excellent fur for evening jackets or coats.

Persian lamb is slightly curly, not very warm, and quite heavy when real. The man made lamb is light and warmer. With this fur the style makes the coat, for the fur itself is not flattering. It also tends to make a woman look old. Mongolian lamb, on the other hand, is very soft and cuddly. Mostly in white/beige with brown patches, or dyed in a variety of colours, it is usually better in a jacket than a whole coat, as it is busy-looking.

This simple mink coat is very versatile and flattering for any woman

You might tire of it quickly. This lamb is warm, but because it is bulky it is not for heavier figures.

Wolf or Coyote

This fur has become the latest fashion craze, and not without reason. It is lovely, rugged, and sexy. White/yellow to grey with darker markings, it is attractive and eye-catching for both women and men. In a full coat, wolf or coyote looks bulky and should be worn only by a tall person. A small woman might consider a short jacket with a hood for sportswear. Since this fur is sporty, it is not suitable for dressy evening wear.

NOTE | Garments made from fur pieces – paws, heads, or other fur ends – are not good investments. They will not wear well and they are very bulky. They are less expensive, it's true, but since you are already spending a lot, the extra money for full skins will be worth it in the long run.

Fox, Lynx, Sable, and Chinchilla

These are luxurious furs and since they have an image of luxury are not for everyday wear, I call them the limousine and chauffeur furs. Sitting in a bus (not to mention a subway) will not do. For these furs you have to be tall, too (5 feet 5 inches and up). A smaller woman will not do herself justice by wearing a lynx coat. For her the most flattering of furs is the mink.

CHOOSING A STYLE

When it comes to the style of an all-purpose fur, the best shapes are the wraparound, straight or slightly fitted, double-breasted, or straight with a mandarin collar (good for the small woman). All are timeless and acceptable for any occasion. The fit should be as good as that of a cloth coat and the same rules for suitability apply. A fur coat should fall softly from the shoulders and make you look slim, not heavy or bulky.

Vertically worked skins are slimming while horizontally worked furs are awkward unless you're tall.

The best length for a fur coat is two or three inches longer than your skirts. If a coat is longer than this you won't look becoming while wearing it with pumps or evening sandals. A fur coat that's too long will dwarf even the tallest woman.

FUR TRIMMINGS

If you can't or don't want to buy a fur coat, you don't have to miss out on the softness and sensual feeling of fur. Try a fling, a silver fox, a stole, a collar, cuffs, or a hat.

NOTE | If you wear a fur hat with a fur coat or jacket, or even with a garment that sports a fur collar, the furs should match. Unfortunately, one often sees a raccoon coat with a mink hat. Combinations like this are not only poorly co-ordinated, but they have no elegance.

FUR JACKETS

If you own a fur coat, a fur jacket could be your second choice. Jackets are very versatile. They can be worn with jeans and they look smashing for sporty or everyday events. A fur jacket can also be worn over a long dress (and it will look much better than a

street-length coat). When worn with pants they are very sexy.

For a very small woman 5 feet and under, a jacket is sometimes the only way she can wear fur. Mink or muskrat would be the most appropriate because they will not overpower her. The correct length is slightly longer than the hip bone, or to the top of the thighs.

Before fur became a fashion it was worn for its warmth.

If you have ever worn a fur, you know that there is nothing that protects you better against cold and wind. The feeling of warmth, softness, and comfort we experience when looking at or touching fur explains why it is one of the most sensuous of all materials. It is extremely flattering for the face and makes a woman look soft and feminine.

6

Soft Blouses and Sexy Sweaters

The right blouse or sweater can carry you from morning to midnight. To do so, however, it has to be of superior quality; first, to stand up to the constant wear, and second, to have the classic style that will look right anywhere. The investment in quality will repay itself many times.

Since blouses and sweaters are separates, like skirts and pants, they can provide you with endless changes and combinations. How becoming they are depends on how well you coordinate them. The expression 'well put together' is really very fitting. We do in fact put these pieces together. And when colours, fabric types, and styles are carefully assembled, the result will be a 'together' look.

The appropriateness of a blouse or sweater is determined mainly by the fabric. For example, a shirt, which is not usually a style for evening, becomes one when made of silk. A loose turtleneck in Shetland wool is sporty but it becomes an evening look when made of angora.

LOOK AT YOUR FIGURE

Before deciding what style and fabric to choose, consider the following details.

Your Neck

If your neck is not as smooth as it used to be, don't draw attention to it by wearing styles that lead the eye to that part of you. Jewel necks, mock turtlenecks, and other round styles draw attention to that area by framing it. Equally bad are scarves or ties wrapped tightly around the neck. They accentuate the problem by adding more wrinkles.

To avoid this, the best look is an open neckline, either through a V-neck design or by leaving the top two or three buttons of your blouse (or dress)open.

For a short neck, open styles give the illusion of length. Collars should lie flat. One that stands up gives the impression that your head is sitting on your shoulders.

NOTE	A short hairstyle is preferable for anyone with a short neck.

Your Arms

A firm arm can afford to wear short-sleeve sweaters or blouses. As a matter of fact, a well-toned arm looks quite sexy. But if your upper arms are a little flabby (and this is often the case, even with thin arms) or are heavier than you find appealing, don't insist on exposing them. Nor do short sleeves look attractive on women with very thin arms.

Tight sleeves are out for both skinny and heavy arms. On the former they will make the arm look skinnier and on the latter they will give the impression of a sausage-like appearance. Choose easy-fitting sleeves with some fullness. A woman with heavy arms should avoid elastic at the wrist as it cuts into the flesh; stay with cuffs. A skinny arm, on the other hand, should always have the sleeve tight at the wrist, either with a cuff or an elastic band.

As you can see, arms play an important role in how a woman looks. I find it surprising that, considering the difference they can make, arms take a back seat when it comes to figure priorities.

If you have long arms and find that most blouses or shirts don't come to your wrist, buy men's shirts; the arms are cut longer and if you pick a tapered style, they look very good on women too. Many women have told me that their shirt cuffs never show because they can't find blouses with the sleeves long enough. Well, this is the solution. You might also be surprised to know that men's silk shirts are less expensive than women's silk blouses.

French cuffs look more feminine than regular ones, and do make a fashion statement. On the practical side, cuffs protect your jacket from undue soil and frequent cleaning.

Your Bust

There is no doubt that a small bust is easier to fit. But a larger bust has its appeal, too. I have always felt that a SLIM SMALL-BUSTED WOMAN looks better dressed, while a woman with a rounder figure looks better undressed. I suppose you can't eat your cake and have it too.

For the SMALL-BUSTED WOMAN a tight-fitting sweater or a blouse with darts is a mistake. You are better off with a rather full look. For the MEDIUM-SIZE WOMAN with a 36-inch bust I have only one suggestion: don't hide yourself. Pick the styles that make the most of your assets in a discreet way – maybe a well-fitting shirt or a sweater that is tight but does not hug you too closely.

For the LARGER WOMAN with a cleavage I suggest wearing loosely fitting styles with the fullness coming from a yoke rather than from the shoulders. Stay with soft fabrics, not stiff ones.

SOFT BLOUSES

This garment, more than any other, can create a mystique about a woman. Apart from the styles that are made to reveal as much as possible, the most sensual blouse for daywear is one with long sleeves that is not transparent. (If your underwear can be seen, even though it is pretty, the look is not appropriate for daytime.) A loosely fitting blouse looks more becoming than one that fits tightly. I don't mean that it should hang over your shoulders or bunch under your arms, but it should allow some fullness over the bust. A blouse looks sexier when worn inside a skirt or pants. But if it's tucked in too tightly, the result will be austere. The look you want is casual and relaxed. The best way to get it is to tuck your blouse or shirt firmly in, pulling it down from underneath (if you're wearing a skirt). Once it is very straight, lift both arms up over your head. This movement will pull the top out far enough to make it look unconstrained, without blousing it too much.

NOTE	For a short-waisted woman, blousing the top extends her upper torso by at least one inch.

TYPES OF FABRIC

Since the material is so important in defining the appropriateness of a blouse, I would like to mention the most important ones.

Silk

Silk is one of the most seductive fabrics a woman can wear. Its softness gives the impression of skin being loosely (and barely) covered. Silk is also flattering because the shine it often has lightens up the face.

When the label reads '100% silk,' it always seems to assure us of quality. Silk is associated with luxury, perhaps because it was first worn only by royalty and the nobility. But '100% silk' alone is not really a guarantee of quality, because silk comes in many different weights. The lighter, rather flimsy type common in blouses from India and Hong Kong, is an inexpensive type. A good-quality silk is one that has body. This type will wear well and always look good. Raw silk, so called because it feels coarser, looks somewhat like linen and is excellent for suits or dresses. The most seductive type for evening wear is silk satin.

The main reason a lot of women don't buy silk blouses, aside from the original purchase price, is the need for dry cleaning, which adds a lot to the price of the blouse. Some silks say 'hand wash' but even if a silk is washable, I advise against it. Washing dulls the fabric and makes it limp.

Here are a few hints on how a silk blouse can serve you better:

- Buy a larger size. The looser fit will make it possible for you to wear the blouse several times before cleaning. Because of the suppleness of the fabric falling gently around your body, no one will notice that the garment is a little on the large side.
- Buy a subdued print rather than a solid colour. It is not as fragile and you can wear it more often. The smallest drop of water is enough to make a spot on a solid shade.
- If perspiration stains have spoiled your beautiful beige silk blouse so that you can't wear it anymore, dye it. Department stores sell dyes for home use. Follow the instructions and, voilá, you can have a brand new red blouse. A word of warning about your underwear: don't wear your new white lace bra under a dyed garment, because the new colour may come off and stain it. Darker lingerie will solve this problem.

Silk can be worn in a simple style in the daytime and in a more elaborate style – maybe with lace trim – anywhere in the evening. It looks as good with jeans as with a velvet suit. The same blouse can be worn with a suit to work and with a different skirt and accessories to give it a dressier appearance in the evening. As you can see, a good silk blouse can go a long way, around the clock and from Monday through Sunday.

| When you find a blouse or shirt that fits and suits you extremely well, buy several in different colours. I can assure you that no one will notice that your white blouse is the same as your brown one. | **NOTE** |

Polyester and Nylon Fabrics
There are many types of synthetics available for blouses. They are so close to silk that in many cases one has to look twice to see what

it is. Synthetics can, of course, be washed by machine, but washing by hand will preserve their look longer. Synthetics are not as supple as natural fibres and unless you buy a more expensive kind you will not feel too comfortable in them, because they won't stay in place. Polyester and nylon also make you feel hot, so a mixture with cotton (60% to 40%) is often more comfortable.

Cotton

There is no cleaner, fresher feeling than putting on a nicely pressed pure cotton blouse or shirt. But who wants to iron these days? Sending shirts to the laundry adds extra expense. (I have never understood why laundries charge twice as much for women's shirts as for men's. Isn't a shirt a shirt?) A cotton-polyester mixture will give you the look without the work, although a little pressing will spruce up the collar and cuffs. A cotton blouse or shirt with a suit or jacket is useful for daywear, and when worn with pants it gives a more casual look.

Rayon

In the old days rayon was regarded as a cheap fabric. It crushes terribly, but is a soft falling material. Because of this latter characteristic, it has gained popularity again, as much in blouses as in dresses. It also feels comfortable and can be worn for day or evening wear.

Crepe

This is a very popular fabric, due to its softness and pliable characteristic without being flabby. It can be worn from morning to evening and looks well in very diverse styles.

THE WHITE BLOUSE

A white blouse is an absolute must. It is one of the most adaptable garments you can own since it's suitable for any time of day and coordinates well with all colours and styles. It is the natural partner of suits, especially a black suit. It will always be the answer to any emergency or unexpected invitation, and makes any woman look younger and fresher. If, as a HEAVY WOMAN, you shy away from this light colour, just remember that under a suit or jacket only a small part is seen, mainly the collar and cuffs.

Off-white is not as effective as white when it comes to a fresh, youthful look. It can make a pale or fair-haired woman look wishy-washy. Cream, on the other hand, compliments most women because it is an extremely soft shade that still has vitality.

STYLES IN BLOUSES

The Shirt

The really classic style is made like a man's shirt, with a band between collar and neckline. This has a sporty look, and unless it is made in silk, it's not suitable for evening. But in cotton (or mixtures thereof) it is good for day and casual wear.

A more feminine and versatile shirt is the one without a band. It can be worn during the daytime or after dark.

Both styles look sexy when made with pockets on the bust. Pockets here are excellent for SMALL-BUSTED WOMEN and increase the sex appeal for a BETTER-ENDOWED WOMAN. A LARGE-BUSTED WOMAN should stay away from this style if she doesn't want to draw attention to her bust line.

A shirt looks attractive with pants as well as with skirts. For the most sensual look, it should be tucked into pants and worn with a belt to complete the look. To keep the edge of the shirt (or any top worn inside) from showing through your pants, tuck it into your pantyhose and you will have a smooth look.

Shirts can also be worn as jackets over T-shirts, either completely open or with the ends knotted at the waist. Make sure that the shirt picks up the colour of the skirt, pulling the look together. If it is not co-ordinated well, you will look as if you were wearing odds and ends you found in your closet.

Peasant Blouses

This style became popular in the 1940s and has since been worn in many different ways and materials. It has kept not only its name but also its look of simple country charm. When the neck is elasticised, it can be pulled down to become an off-the-shoulder style.

A peasant style will help a SMALL-BUSTED WOMAN look bigger. It gives a WELL-ENDOWED WOMAN a chance to show off gracefully by pulling down the elastic a bit. For a LARGE-BUSTED WOMAN it can divert the attention when worn with a frill. Again it is sexier and more intriguing when it has long sleeves. Short sleeves give an image of youth and immaturity.

Trousers do not improve the look of a peasant blouse. A slightly gathered skirt with ruffles at the hem completes the soft look this blouse gives.

Blouses with Ties

The tie on most blouses is a scarf attached around the neck. It can frame the neckline and décolletage in a very nice way, but to do so it has to be tied low (as in the picture), rather than high. Some women wrap the tie around the neck, making it look like a bandage.

Blouses with ties are often made to close high at the neck. You can change this by turning the corners in and stitching them down; the scarf part can then be tied where you feel it looks best on you. Its appeal is increased further when made in a very soft fabric. So buy this style in the softest material you can find.

The tie blouse is appropriate for day and evening wear and good for ALL FIGURE TYPES. A HEAVY WOMAN will find that the openness from neck to bust makes her look slimmer. She shouldn't make a bow, however, but just tie the scarf once and let the ends hang down to further elongate the look.

Long Peter Pan Collars

After what I said about Peter Pan collars on dresses, you may think that they're hopeless – not so. The long version of this collar, set

around a V-neck and made in a solid-colour satin or silk, is quite seductive. Because it's an elegant look, this is especially suitable for evening, and looks good worn with a straight or pleated skirt (not an A-line or full skirt). This is one of the few styles that looks good without sleeves. Because the collar lies over the bust, it is beneficial for a SMALL-BUSTED WOMAN.

Mandarin or Band Collars

This is a very suitable style for a short neck or SMALL WOMAN. It does not overwhelm or add extra fabric. It fits under most suits, but it has to be worn open – never close it to the top. For a HEAVY WOMAN, however, it can emphasise her size, since the narrowness of the band collar is not enough to counterbalance the bust. It is an excellent style to be worn unbuttoned, making it look very much like a jacket.

Shawl Collars

Being an elegant look, this is best in silk or crepe. It is a mature style and does not give a young impression. A VERY SMALL-BUSTED WOMAN should not wear it, as the small narrow collar will emphasise her flatness. For exactly that reason it is a good choice for a LARGE-BUSTED WOMAN.

How far open you can wear a blouse or shirt is not decided by the buttons, as you might think, but by you. I know that most of the time a button toward the top closes a shirt too much while the next one down leaves it too far open. To get around this dilemma, close it with a brooch between the button holes.

NOTE

Cowl Necks

The draping of the material is very intriguing and flattering if it is a low cowl. The cowl can fall fairly high around the neck, in between, or very low down. How low you can wear it depends on your bust. A VERY SMALL-BUSTED WOMAN can go as low as she dares. Since her bust will be hidden by the fabric it will make her appear larger at the same time. For a HEAVIER WOMAN it is not a flattering look; the extra fabric makes her look bigger than she is.

This style looks best without sleeves and should be in a very soft fabric like a rayon Jersey; a crisper material makes the folds spring open when you move. This is a style for evening or special occasions, not daywear. It should be worn only with a skirt.

Lace Blouses

It's pretty when there's not too much of it. High-necked, long-sleeved lace blouses with ruffles around the neck are romantic but not overpowering. For a more seductive look the blouse should be open, showing some skin.

It can be worn with a skirt or pants. Since lace is very festive, the skirt or tousers must be in the same mood – made from either silk, satin, or velvet. This is one of the few times your black gabardine or wool pants won't do.

The most becoming lace blouse is either white or cream. Black can easily look too austere unless it is sleeveless and has a big décolletage.

<table>
<tr><td>As lace is transparent, don't wear just a bra under it. Instead try a camisole in a satiny fabric, without lace or other intriguing trimmings; it will help bring out the lace of the blouse. A more daring look is to have the camisole in a different colour; black under white, peach or brown under cream.</td><td>**NOTE**</td></tr>
</table>

Lace can be worn by every slim figure. On a SMALL WOMAN the lace should be dainty and delicate. On a HEAVY WOMAN it will mean too much of a good thing. For her a blouse partially in lace (such as in an insert or trimming) is preferable to all-over lace.

Embroidered Blouses

As far as suitability is concerned, an embroidered blouse is like a lace one – overpowering, unbecoming, and unsexy when there is too much of it, but attractive when the amount is limited. Embroidery on the collar and cuffs is a nice way to add a gentle touch. In moderation it is good for ALL FIGURE TYPES.

Unlike a lace blouse, an embroidered one can be worn in the daytime. And it will look fine with a wool skirt or pants.

Blouses with Frills

A blouse with ruffles is a garment only for dressy or special occasions. As far as suitability goes, everything I said about frills in Chapter 3 applies to a blouse too. The most wearable style is the one made in a soft material which allows the frills to fall easily and move with the body.

Tunics

Strictly speaking, a tunic is not a blouse or shirt, but it often replaces one. Its good qualities are numerous, so it is a fairly constant look on the fashion scene.

Due to a tunic's simple cut and suitability, it is a good style for everyone. It can be worn at home, for casual events, for cocktails, or for an evening on the town. For professional wear, however, it is not an appropriate choice.

Even a SHORT WOMAN can wear a tunic, although she might have to shorten it to fit her proportions. For a TALL SLIM WOMAN the tunic is a fabulous garment to make her look sexy, elegant, and intriguing. It is more seductive worn with pants, hanging loosely over the body. It should reach down to below the thighs and be made from soft fabrics like silk or jersey. This figure type can wear it belted or loose equally well. For a HEAVY WOMAN a tunic will make her feel very comfortable as it covers all and hides all.

For a slimming look the TALL HEAVY WOMAN can wear a tunic down to her calves, but in this case it must have slits at the sides that open to her thighs and be worn over pants. By the way, slits are a plus on any style tunic for ANY FIGURE TYPE.

A well-fitting sweater made of luxurious wool – angora, cashmere, or mohair – has been classified as one of the most seductive of all garments. But a very tight sweater that moulds the body and emphasises the bust is vulgar, not sensual. A sensual sweater says that there is a bust but doesn't give it away.

Apart from being sensual, soft, cuddly, and warm (or cool in the summer), knits are extremely practical. They are wrinkleproof, and easy to care for. They span the seasons as they can be worn in the winter under coats and in the spring or fall by themselves.

A sweater is of course more casual than a blouse but if you stick to styles like turtlenecks or crew necks (worn with a blouse) they are right for business or daywear. It is interesting to note, by the way, that a sweater and skirt look more dressy than a blouse and skirt.

A blouse with a skirt (or pants) never looks quite complete; a third piece in the form of a jacket or blazer seems to be needed. A good sweater and skirt, on the other hand, can easily stand of their own.

A knit top looks better when it's worn outside at the waist rather than tucked in. The length is not important when worn with a skirt. But with pants that have pockets, loops, and maybe pleats, a short style is more becoming.

If you don't usually wear a bra, you might consider it when you wear a sweater. In many cases a knit either flattens the bust or, being very soft, moulds it so that it looks sagging, especially when you aren't sitting or standing perfectly straight. So look at yourself sideways; you might find that a bra would improve your shape. **NOTE**

TYPES OF YARN

The sweaters discussed below come in a great variety of yarns and knits. Natural fibres are the prettiest and most becoming, but unfortunately they are also the most expensive. Synthetics like Orlon, Acrilan, and so on are good alternatives, and are a lifesaver for people who are allergic to wool.

Angora

This is the most seductive one of them all. White increases its luxurious appearance even further. It is not a look for professional situations, but certainly for all others! Being fluffy, it does make a person look bigger, but the extra seduction power usually makes up for the extra inch.

Mohair

This is very similar to angora but not as fluffy or soft. It also makes one look heavier and can be overpowering in bulky styles. It's not a good choice for a SMALL WOMAN or a HEAVY WOMAN.

Bouclè

This, like other textured knits, is good for extra sweaters but not for basic ones. It makes a woman look larger and should therefore be worn only by slimmer figures. Yet for a HEAVY WOMAN this type of knit in a cardigan style or knit suit can look very attractive and flattering.

Cashmere

This yarn is in a class by itself. It has long been regarded as one of the world's luxuries. It originated in Kashmir, India, in the fifteenth century, and that's where it got its name. The fleece comes from a goat. Since cashmere fibre is very thin, it takes the fleece of three goats to make an average-size sweater. No wonder the price is so high!

The cashmere sweater as we know it today was introduced in 1920 and was first made by a Scottish underwear mill in a boxy pullover or cardigan style. Today you can find many different designs in cashmere. But I would suggest that, due to the high price, you buy a conservative style (crew neck, turtleneck, or cardigan) in a basic shade. Provided you take care of it, a cashmere pullover will last you for years and years. It is always in fashion and the image you project will always be favourable – not just because you are wearing an expensive sweater but because its softness will make you look that way, too.

If you own a cashmere sweater, you're aware of the effect this wool has on the senses. Isn't it a pleasure to stroke it and feel its softness against your skin? If you don't own one, do go and look at them, touch them, maybe even try one on. When you see how flattering this knit looks, and feel how its softness caresses you, you might understand, forgive, and accept the price of sixty five pounds and up.

Cotton

This yarn makes it possible for us to wear sweaters as frequently in the summer as in the winter. A sweater made from a cotton is one of the coolest garments you can wear during the warm months. Made in white or cream they are a versatile piece for under suits or just to wear with a skirt or pants. To preserve not only their look but also their size don't wash and dry them in the machine: they will be too small after several cleanings.

BASIC SWEATER STYLES

The following classic styles should be the foundation of your sweater wardrobe. Since they are basic, buy them in the basic colours of your wardrobe.

Turtlenecks

The turtleneck is one of the most becoming and useful styles. Emerging from a jacket, coat, or V-neck blouse, it always completes an outfit. It can be worn in fine knits for daywear and in heavy wools for casual or sportswear. However, to make it look most attractive the collar must be worn high, as high as possible, right up to the chin. Try it the next time you wear your turtleneck and you'll see the difference. (See illustration of classical suit and turtleneck in Chapter 4.)

When you find a style that fits you well buy it in different colours.

NOTE

Short-necked woman usually shy away from this style but unless your neck is extremely short, you too can wear it up to your chin, and in a very fine knit that does not add volume.

For a SLIM TALL WOMAN a belt can change the look of a turtleneck. Wear it loose rather than cinched tight, to give you a more relaxed image.

For a HEAVY WOMAN, tall or short, only turtlenecks in a fine wool should be worn. A fine chain (no heavy pendants) will have a slimming effect. Many women feel that a turtleneck needs jewellry. It really doesn't. A chain or pendants can detract from the total look.

While a mock turtleneck is not flattering a large cowl-neck can be very charming. However, it is not so advantageous for a SMALL WOMAN or a HEAVY WOMAN as it is somewhat bulky. For a TALL WOMAN it is a sweater that can be worn well day or evening.

Crew Necks

By itself the crew neck is not a sexy-looking sweater. But worn with a shirt showing at the collar and cuffs, it is a timeless, charming look for many daytime occasions, and wearable by ALL FIGURE TYPES. Worn under a jacket it even looks good without the shirt. The jacket creates an open V-neck image.

V-Necks

This style is equally attractive when worn by itself with pants or, with a blouse under it, with a skirt. In a dark colour it can be worn for evening with appropriate accessories. Long, hanging earrings emphasise the openness of the V-neck more than chains do.

Cardigans

When it comes to cardigans, some of you probably see a homely image. But there are cardigans and cardigans, and there are different ways to wear them, too. The basic rule is that regardless of figure type, a cardigan should be loose. Button it up when you try it on; there should be no gaps between the buttons.

A cardigan can function as a second layer to keep you warm or as a sweater worn by itself. The V-neck type is the most versatile. It can be worn not only alone or over something, open or closed, but also in the evening. And it looks good on ALL FIGURE TYPES.

A round-neck cardigan acquires a crew-neck look when buttoned, and since the crew neck alone is not the most flattering, this style cardigan looks better worn open. It can also replace a blazer or jacket, but it must be loose.

For a HEAVY WOMAN a cardigan should meet in front when open. You should not have to pull it to close it. And it must be at least hip length.

TWIN SETS

You can combine a crew neck and a cardigan by buying a twin set. The look is one of co-ordination and harmony. As a matter of fact, a skirt with a twin set can even replace a suit on occasions. It can be worn by ALL FIGURE TYPES and even for evening if styled accordingly.

MEN'S SWEATERS

For those of you who can never find a sweater that fits loosely enough, a man's sweater may be the solution. The styles and colours of basic sweaters are identical, and even for a different look, you can often find more interesting designs in a man's department.

Of course if you wear a large size you would take a medium or even small in a man's sweater. But do try them on to make sure they're not too big under the arm.

Now comes the best part: men's sweaters are cheaper than the same style for women. So for the extra few inches or to save a few pounds, don't forget to check out this source.

FANCY SWEATER STYLES

Hooded Sweaters

Everyone says: 'Oh, how nice' when they see a sweater with a hood – but few women own one. The reason has to do with limited use. As the hood doesn't look good under a coat or jacket, the sweater can be worn only during in-between seasons. The use of the hood itself is practically nil. Hardly anyone ever wears it and if they do, it looks unattractive.

This is not a good style for a HEAVY WOMAN. If you do consider buying one, remember that it is an unusual look, not an everyday one.

Scoopeneck Sweaters

This style of sweater looks becoming on every woman, but should never be worn over a blouse. When it is – and it's not uncommon – the look is 'homemade,' not stylish. The wearer seems to have done a poor job of putting herself together.

Bulky Sweaters

Bulky tops should always be with skinny bottoms – in other words, with pants, and narrow ones at that; baggy styles will make the wearer look big all over. Yet a loose bulky sweater with a pair of tapered jeans looks very sexy.

How successfully you can achieve this look depends on your figure. The main criterion here is slimness. Long legs are a plus, too. For the HEAVY WOMAN a loosely fitting cardigan style (with straight pants) is preferable.

Bulky sweaters or cardigans are often made in a multitude of colours. The look can be pretty and exciting, but because most people probably own only one or two bulky sweaters, it's better to buy them in subdued tones. If you can afford several, however, by all means get one in bright red, blue, yellow, or green.

Long Sweaters

Made in the style of a tunic, these sweaters are a nice change. They are good for casual wear with pants or for daywear over a skirt. They are not appropriate for the office.

For a SMALL SLIM WOMAN this sweater should be no longer than the top of her thighs and as plain as possible. For the SMALL HEAVY WOMAN an overblouse going to the hips is a better choice, again without trimmings.

A long sweater is a sexy look for a TALL SLIM WOMAN. She can afford to wear it at any length and with any trimmings (such as patch pockets). It looks becoming belted or loose. For a TALL HEAVY WOMAN a plain design and hip length is better. For ALL FIGURE TYPES this sweater must be loose to fall easily over the body.

Evening Sweaters

An after-dark look is created by the yarn and trimmings. For example, a turtleneck with gold threads woven through it is an evening sweater. (Despite the relaxation in rules about what can be worn where, I still feel that glitter in any form should not be worn during the day.)

Evening sweaters include pretty V-necks, boat necks, and many other designs made in angora or with gold and silver trimmings. A more extravagant look is achieved with feathers or appliqued flowers. How extravagant you want to be depends on the occasion. As far as style is concerned, the same rules apply as for a daytime sweater.

A sweater worn in the evening can not only give a nice change to your look, but can also save you some money, as it is usually cheaper than a whole outfit.

Summer Sweaters

As warm and cosy as a sweater is in the winter, it can be just as cool in the summer.

The Italians have been known for their knits for a long time, but I think they are especially gifted when it comes to cotton and silky summer knits. Without hesitation I would say that no one makes more attractive lightweight knits and summer sweaters. They are not cheap, but the fine styling and durability make them worth the price.

Silky, shiny-looking yarns are especially appealing. A shiny turquoise yarn can make the plainest style (a boat neck with short sleeves, for instance) very appealing.

A silky or loose type of knit is also more prone to snag than tightly woven wool. Whenever a thread does pull, don't cut it. Carefully stretch the area of the snag and then pull the extra thread out the back.

I should add a few words of warning about loosely knit tops or open-work designs. Like transparent blouses, these let your lingerie be seen. Often a sweater doesn't lend itself to being worn with a camisole, and a bra peeking through will not look sensual. You might prefer to stay away from open knits.

General Hints For:

SMALL BUST
30"–32"

- Never wear a sweater that fits very tightly, or has skinny ribs.
- Bouclè or other textured knits are good; so are cable knits.
- Fluffy wools like angora and mohair and all other types of wools as well are fine if not worn tight.
- You can blouse your sweaters a bit by wearing belts with them.

MEDIUM-SIZE BUST
34"–36"

- You have all the options you want. You can wear any style, knit type, or yarn. Keep in mind what makes a sweater look sexy.

LARGE BUST
38" plus

- For you fine yarns and plain knit styles are best.
- A narrow rib can be slimming if it's not made in a heavy wool.
- Stay away from cable knits or other heavy designs.

As you can see, blouses and sweaters in a myriad different forms and styles can do a lot to make your wardrobe versatile and appropriate. To make them bring out your sensual side, choose the styles and fabrics that bring out your assets best. Remember that you want to look comfortable and at ease with yourself, not buttoned up, self-conscious, or hidden away under layers of clothing. (If you are cold with just a turtleneck, wear a T-shirt under it; this will not disturb the image as would a blouse or vest worn over it.

Don't forget that the top of your outfit sets the mood for the look. The skirt or pants must harmonise with it.

7

Feminine Skirts and Pants

Wearing the most becoming skirts and pants means wearing anything too tight, too short, or too revealing. It does mean wearing styles that allow your legs and hips to be seen favourably.

A skirt or a pair of pants complete the look of softness and femininity that begins with your blouse or sweater. Matching the two in style is not difficult if you keep in mind that it is the fabric more than the design that determines suitability. An A-line skirt in a tweed material will not match a lace blouse, but an A-line skirt in silk or satin will look right. A pleated skirt in a fine wool fabric will look better with a silk blouse than with a cotton shirt. A bulky sweater needs jeans or a pair of wool pants, not a cotton or silky fabric.

NOTE   A nearly foolproof material for avoiding mistakes and achieving good matches is a gabardine in wool or a mixture of wool and polyester. You can wear a sweater or silk blouse equally well with it.

Since skirts and pants are staple items, their colours should be in the two or three basic shades around which your wardrobe is built, as discussed in Chapter 1.

LET'S LOOK FIRST AT SKIRTS

Whereas a pair of pants can make us feel sexy and sure of ourselves, a sensuous skirt can make a woman feel feminine and fragile. Like the skirt of a dress, it should flow and move with the body. However, a skirt by itself should fit well around the hips so it flatters your figure. The height of a skirt can enhance your image or ruin it.

Before I talk about the different styles here are some important points that apply to all skirt designs and to ALL FIGURE TYPES:

1. A skirt with lining is better than one without. Lining increases your skirt's lifespan and gives it support so it will hang better. Many summer skirts are not lined and are so transparent that they reveal the shape of the body underneath. This might sound sexy, but in reality it is too blatant for daily wear. With skirts like this, wear a slip.

2. Make sure that the length of the skirt is correct. I've already pointed out the importance of length, but I'd like to emphasise again that the only right length is the one that makes your legs look their best.

   A skirt that's too long makes a heavy leg look heavier, and makes any woman look older.

3. Although the mini seems to be here to stay remember that knees are not one of a women's most attractive features. But you can afford this look if your legs are slim and trim, without marks or veins.

4. Skirts look better when worn with a belt. It finishes the look and adds interest. If you are short, you may think that a belt cuts you in two. This is true only if it is a different colour from your skirt. Match the belt to the garment. If you're wearing a navy-blue skirt, your belt should be navy blue too, perhaps with some gold trimming or a nice buckle. It should be no wider than an inch and a half.

These feminine separates can work in various combinations for evening or daytime wear.

116

HEAVY WOMEN tend to shy away from belts. They feel that a belt will make their waist look bigger. Not so. At least, not when you wear a jacket or vest, which means that only the buckle and a few inches on either side of the belt are visible, as on our picture.

The MEDIUM-TO-TALL SLIM WOMAN can wear any type of belt, but a soft leather one is more becoming than a wide, rigid one which will make you look stiff around the waist.

The A-Line Skirt

This skirt fits around the hips and flares out toward the hem. It can be made with several panels or from just two pieces. The fullness varies. A SLIM WOMAN can wear a slightly more flowing type, while a MEDIUM or HEAVY WOMAN will look better in a more moderate A-line. This style looks good on ANY FIGURE TYPE. It also fits easily with any type of jacket.

Dirndl or Gathered Skirt

This model is gathered around the waist and falls straight down, often with pockets in the side seams. How much gathering you can afford and where the gathers are depend on your figure. If your stomach protrudes at all, avoid fullness in front and instead have the gathers off centre and in the back. If you are hippy, gathers should be in the front and back. A HEAVY WOMAN should have only a very slight shirring to give an otherwise straight skirt some fullness. The SLIM WOMAN with narrow hips can afford all the gathers she wants, where she wants.

Full-Circle Skirt

A complete circle makes the hips look wide. This style should be worn only by a TALL, VERY SLIM WOMAN who does not fill out the fabric. And even for her, the material must be very soft so that it hangs easily and closely around the body.

The Straight Skirt

This style fits closely around the hips and continues straight down to the hem. It can be worn by ALL FIGURE TYPES, except for a VERY SLIM WOMAN; on her it will not be attractive because it will make her look too skinny.

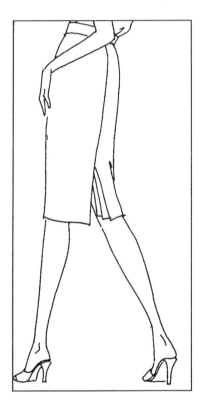 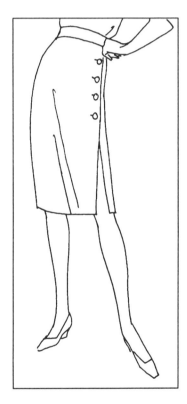

Skirt with Slits

A slit is there to show your legs, not your underwear. Even though a slip may not be visible when you stand still, it often shows when you walk or sit – yes, even if it has a slit in the same place as the one in your skirt. (Seeing your underwear detracts from the purpose of the slit.) What can you do? Buy a half-slip that stops just above the slit; if you can't find one, shorten a long one.

Since slits reveal the legs, make sure that your legs are a feature you want to emphasise. If they're heavy, you might want to avoid slits and draw attention to your décolletage instead.

Where should a slit be? A slit up the back or front tends to make a woman look cheap unless it is partially hidden by a pleat; if there is extra material, it will prevent too much exposure and thus add subtlety (as in preceeding picture). A slit off centre on either side is the least becoming, as it exposes the knees. A slit up one side of the skirt is the most sensual and also the one with which you can be most daring. It can go right up to your hip for an evening look or beach outfit. But be careful with slits on both sides; they tend to make a person look larger, even if they are quite short.

Buttoned-Down Skirts

This style, besides being pretty and easy to get in and out of, is good for any figure. For a SMALL WOMAN it elongates the body. For a MEDIUM-SIZE WOMAN the style makes an interesting change in her wardrobe. For a HEAVY WOMAN this model helps draw attention away from the hips to the middle of the skirt. (But she has to make sure that the skirt is ample enough so it doesn't pull or gap in front.) For a more tantalising look for any size woman, a few buttons can be left open at the bottom.

NOTE | With this style, whatever you wear on top must be tucked in. Buttoned-down skirts look good only when the waist can be seen.

Wraparound Skirts

The wraparound skirt looks feminine and is easy to wear. The most becoming design is the one that closes at the front, halfway between the centre and side seams. A closing in the back is not as flattering and it can lead to worry that the wind will expose us. ALL FIGURE TYPES can wear wraparounds, but if you are a larger size and don't feel at ease in one, don't wear it.

120

Pleated Skirts

Skirts can be pleated in many different ways: all around, in the front or back, or on the side only. There are pleats that open at the waist and others that open below the hips. A pleated or partially pleated skirt is most feminine, but the type of pleats and where they are positioned depends on your figure. A SLIM HIPPED WOMAN can wear pleats all around, starting at the waist, as well as any other types of pleats. A MEDIUM-BUILD WOMAN should choose pleats that are closed to the hips and then open below.

The idea that pleats are unbecoming for a HEAVY WOMAN is false. Of course she shouldn't wear a skirt with pleats opening from the waist, but pleats stitched down, opening on the lower part of the skirt, add movement and a youthful touch

ABOUT POCKETS

Doesn't it feel good to bury your hands in your pockets? For this reason, pockets help our self-confidence. But unless they are the right type they won't make you look better. Here are my choices:

- *Slanted pockets* (from the waist diagonal to the side seam) are a nice detail, but only for the woman with NARROW HIPS. These pockets will make women with BIG HIPS look larger.
- *Patch pockets*. For a SHORT WOMAN I advise against them. A MEDIUM-TO-TALL SLIM WOMAN can wear them well and they will add volume and roundness to the silhouette. A HEAVY WOMAN can consider them only on an A-line skirt where they are set low.
- *Side-seam pockets* are the most common and suitable for every figure. But do make sure that the skirt is not so tight that the outline of the pocket shows through.

GOOD-LOOKING PANTS

It has been said that an attractive woman looks even more appealing in men's clothing. The millions of women wearing pants today certainly prove it. However, for a pair of pants to be flattering they must at all times fit well. Styles like baggy jeans or those that add extra fullness through gathers (such as drawstring pants) are less becoming, except on a very slim woman.

Today it is hard to remember that pants were not always a standard item for women. But years ago women wearing pants were not allowed into certain restaurants, and only in the early 1970s could female office workers wear them to work. Actually, pants were not always part of male attire either, but man's chance came long before ours.

A BRIEF HISTORY

Trousers originated somewhere in Central Asia. By about 1700 B.C. the ancient Persians were wearing fitted coats, boots, and long tight trousers. But Europeans did not adopt the style. The Greeks and Romans wore draped clothes, and so did the people of the early Middle Ages. Later, fitted hose and tunics became the fashion, but only for men. (One of the charges that sent Joan of Arc to her death was that she had worn men's clothes.)

Pants did not become popular in Europe until the Renaissance. The Venetians included a character called 'Pantalone' in their *commedia dell'arte* theatre. The men playing this role always wore baggy trousers. Not only did this stage character popularise the look, but he also gave his name to them – known as *pantalon* in French and pants in English. For a long time, however, the preferred pants for men were breeches, which ended just below the knee. (From this look comes the still-current knickerbockers, or knickers.) The main exceptions were specialised garments, like sailors' bell-bottoms.

It was not until about 1800 that men's pants came down to the ankles. The only women to wear pants at this time were those in some regions of the Middle and Far East. For the women of America, the first step toward pants was made by Amelia Jenks Bloomer in 1851, who encouraged women to shorten their skirts and wear pants under them – a type of trouser named after her. The model called bloomers today lacks any hint of sensuality, but Mrs. Bloomer herself did not.

In the 1930s women began to wear pants for sports and leisure wear. Then, during World War II, more women started wearing slacks as practical everyday garments. The 1950s brought stretch pants and toreador pants. Then with the 1960s came a generation that seemed to wear nothing *but* pants; this was the youth revolution that popularised blue jeans.

As often when changes occur, fashion is pushed to an extreme first, and then adjusts to a more moderate path. The jean revolution helped pants become acceptable for any occasion and lifestyle, but in the 1970s skirts staged a comeback. Today skirts and pants are just about interchangeable, with emphasis varying somewhat from season to season and according to personal preference.

JEANS, JEANS, AND MORE JEANS

Without doubt jeans are the sexiest pants ever made, leaving nothing about your figure to the imagination. Levi Straus was the first one to make them with rivets and extra stitching for greater durability. (Miners out West needed strong pockets to hold their mineral samples.) But the name 'jeans' originated in Italy during the fifteenth century, when sailors wore pants made from a heavy cloth called Genoa fustian – *jean fustian* in French.

Since that time, jeans have truly become the uniform of the world. They are now worn by both sexes, by every age group, and by every nationality. They successfully bridge social, racial, and economic barriers. Every time they seem to have reached their peak of popularity, something happens to push it upward – when couturiers started making designer jeans they became acceptable for even the most sceptical among us. Jeans are now made from a great variety of fabrics and in many different colours, but the most popular is still the real blue jean of denim.

The image of jeans is tall and lean, so the slimmer you are the better they will look on you. But since they are a sign of comfort and a youthful attitude, they are worn by every figure type.

How to Buy Jeans

I don't know if the fact that there are countless different designs and brands available makes it easier or harder to find the right pair. I do know that when I buy jeans, I have to try on at least six pairs before finding the right one. Designer jeans have made it easier, as they are cut for a woman's body, but a lot of women still have trouble getting the right fit.

Jeans, unlike other pants, should be snug, especially around the hips and thighs. They lose their image if they don't hug you tightly. The best fabric is the preshrunk type.

When you look for jeans, try different brand names, from the designers to the Levis. (If you're lucky you will find a pair of Wranglers or a similar make that will cost you less than any of the designer styles.)

Different makes will give you a wide range in cut and fit. Once you have found a make and size that suits you, try a smaller size, a bigger size, and another pair of the same size. It's the only way to make sure that you get the best fit, because even pants labelled the same size can vary. Don't feel discouraged: jeans are *by far* the most difficult pants to buy – unless you're a size 8 with narrow hips.

If the waist is too big, say one inch (but not more), you can pull it in with your belt. (By the way, a belt is just as important an accessory for pants as it is for skirts. Many women omit belts with jeans, but it gives the impression of not being completely dressed, of having forgotten something.)

Jeans should hug your hips and thighs. If there are pleats in the back below your derrière, it is not a good fit. On the other hand, if they hug you too tightly, they will flatten your derrière so that you won't look sexy. Remember, even a 'snug fit' means that you must be able to sit down. I've heard of one store where they help a customer into jeans by having her lie down so that a saleswoman can zip the pants closed.

From the knee down, the shape of the legs changes according to fashion trends. The boot leg (so called because it is worn inside a boot) is 16 inches wide at the bottom. A straight leg, worn over boots, is 17 inches wide. Flares and bell-bottoms are wider still.

NOTE	Bell-bottoms are not a good choice for a HEAVY WOMAN or a SMALL WOMAN.

Because jeans are one item in your wardrobe that should be fashionable (avoid very narrow legs when straight legs are in), don't buy too many. You don't need more than two pairs of blue denims, plus maybe one or two in different colours. (I always found black very useful for winter.) And you don't have to keep three old pairs for cleaning or other dirty work; one pair will do.

How to Care for Jeans

To make jeans fit better and to adjust them to your body, there are a few tricks you can try:

1. If you want a pair of jeans to look as if you'd been poured into them, put them on and sit in the bathtub (preferably in warm water) to get them completely wet. Then let the water drip off and get out of them carefully, hanging them up to dry. When they are nearly dry, put them on again and keep them on. This is admittedly quite a production but it really works. I have even stretched tight jeans this way. I put them on wet and after a few knee bends was able to close the zipper.
2. If you have a pair that fits nicely, don't spoil the new look by washing; dry clean the jeans instead. When you've paid twenty-five pounds or more, they deserve dry cleaning.
3. When washing jeans, you can prevent shrinkage by not putting them in the dryer. This precaution should be taken even with preshrunk materials. The reverse works too. If you lose weight and you want your jeans to lose weight too, by all means put them in the dryer.
4. To look slimmer in jeans, iron in a pleat; it makes the leg look slimmer.
5. Do not, I repeat *not*, turn the excess length into cuffs. They will make your legs look shorter. A lot of women do it, but they look

stubby, not long-legged. If you can't find the right length, have them shortened, or just cut them off neatly.

6. For the HEAVY TALL or SMALL WOMAN, there are now jeans made in stretch denim that will solve any fit problems.

Apropos of ironing jeans, I feel that jeans have gotten a bad name because they are often worn without being ironed or properly cared for. Many people think they don't have to be washed too often, let alone pressed, and that they can be frayed or patched and really look good only when ready to be thrown away. But do jeans in the sexy ads look like that? Of course not. They are clean and pressed, and give an image of being taken care of.

If you consider buying a pair of corduroy or velvet jeans, remember that these fabrics add weight, so unless you are slim enough to get by, stay with smoother, flatter materials.

CONSERVATIVE PANTS

The conservative design is one that every woman can wear and should have in her wardrobe. Being very basic, these pants are versatile and practical and are best in a wool or gabardine (or a mixture thereof). They have straight legs, no pleats and a narrow waistband. Regardless of your size keep the following in mind:

1. A straight leg means that from the heaviest part of your thigh the leg should continue straight down, not be tapered or flared. Therefore, how wide a straight leg is at the bottom is determined by the size of the thigh.
2. A narrow waistband – one inch or so – is at all times more flattering than one of two inches or more, which will make you look heavier.

Other details like pockets and pleats depend on your figure type. If you have:

NARROW HIPS

• You can afford to wear pleated pants and slanted pockets. They will give shape and roundness to your hips without disturbing the fit or the back of the pants. (See

127

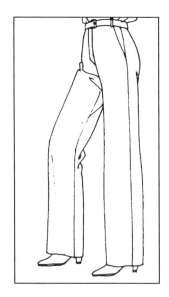

picture of pleated pants, page 148.)

MEDIUM HIPS

LARGE HIPS

• Pleated styles will make you look bigger but you can wear slanted pockets.

• Avoid pleats and slanted pockets. Even pockets in the side seams can be unbecoming as they often gap and add bulk to the hips. A pocket that is horizontal with the waistband would make for a better look. If you find a pair of pants that fit well and the slanted pockets are the only drawback, close them up.
Stitch along the edge and then cut out the fabric of the pocket.

NOTE | For large hips and thighs the best style is the straight leg. Bell-bottoms add bulk and tapered narrow legs emphasise the hips too much.

pants can therefore be altered without trouble. And believe me, nobody ever notices that the flap over the zipper faces the 'wrong' way. (Nobody ever told me that I was wearing men's pants.) In any case, we find it perfectly acceptable when wearing jeans.

If you feel shy about going into the men's department of a big store, try a boutique that has individual fitting rooms. Women who wear men's pants – I mean that literally – are much more common than you might think.

Cuffs

Every so often fashion presents us with cuffed pants, but they never gain wide acceptance. Personally, I always feel that cuffed pants say 'menswear.' Leaving my own opinion aside, a cuff does shorten your leg. As I've said before, long legs are regarded as a plus, so cuffs detract from this objective. For a SMALL WOMAN it will make her look shorter. For the HEAVIER WOMAN cuffs add bulk, which she does not want. That leaves the TALL SLIM WOMAN, who can follow her preference.

OTHER STYLES

Apart from jeans and conservative pants, there are many other styles to choose from.

Pleated Pants

So called because this style has one or two pleats in front. The fullness that is added through the pleats makes them look baggy and prevents the shape of the hips from being seen. A good style for women with too-straight hips, it will give an illusion of roundness. But if you have full hips, this style will not make you look slimmer.

Certain other details can make a big difference in how well pants contribute to your look.

Length

A pair of conservative pants should touch your instep in front and slope down toward the back to cover half your heel.

Because the height of your heels affects the length of your pants you have to decide what shoes you want to wear with them. To test whether the length is correct, take a few steps. If too much of your foot can be seen or if the pants legs slip into your shoes, the pants are too short. On the other hand, if the pants cover the heel completely and touch the floor, you will look as if you have no feet at all!

Rise

The rise (distance from the waist to the crotch) is important. The crotch of the pants should not be lower than your own. If it is, you will be uncomfortable and will look heavier; your legs will look shorter, too.

For a woman who is short from the waist to the crotch, men's pants are a solution, because they are cut shorter in the rise. If you are worried about the waist being too big, remember that men's pants are made in such a way that a waist adjustment is anticipated;

Tapered Pants

As far as sensuality is concerned, ankle-length tapered pants are second only to jeans, provided they are worn with high-heeled shoes. The slim line makes the legs appear longer and draws attention in a subtle way to the hips. For this reason only SLIM-HIPPED WOMEN should wear this style.

Harem Pants

For leisure wear (at home or at the beach), full harem pants, pulled in and tied just at the ankles, are very seductive. How could they be otherwise, since seduction was their original purpose! Because it is often difficult to find the right top, I recommend that you buy these pants only when there is a top available to go with them. It is not a good style for a HEAVY WOMAN or a SHORT WOMAN.

This type of pants should always be made in a soft, flowing fabric. Even a slim woman will look heavy in a bulkier fabric because of the amount of material used for this style. | **NOTE**

Culottes or Divided Skirts

Culottes, though usually around in one form or another, are never widely accepted – probably because most women feel that they do not enhance their figures. Badly cut culottes emphasise the crotch in a manner that is unflattering and vulgar. And even culottes made like a skirt are not flattering. If you don't believe me, just ask your favourite man what he thinks of them; you'll never wonder about them again!

Knickers, Jodhpurs, and Short Trousers

These styles are fun and appropriate for young girls, but they aren't suitable (or even dignified) on grown women. The fact that they stop either just below the knee or halfway down the calf shortens the legs and makes them look unbecoming. For a SHORT WOMAN they are simply a disaster.

Leather Pants

Have you always dreamed of owning a pair of leather pants, but been unable to because they're so expensive? Well, don't feel bad; you haven't missed a thing. Leather pants are very, very warm and not as comfortable as they look. They make you appear and feel heavier, which is the reason that only very thin women can look attractive in them (and then only if they are made of a very fine-quality leather).

A FEW ADDITIONAL POINTS

It is not attractive to see panty lines through the fabric of your pants or to see where a girdle stops. To avoid this, wear only pantyhose or a long-legged girdle. If you feel uncomfortable without panties, buy Underalls, which have a panty top, or use a tissue liner.

One of the main reasons why pants have become so popular is the comfort they offer. When it comes to sports, leisure wear, or travelling, there is nothing more comfortable than a pair of pants. It is interesting to note that when a man wants to lounge or be comfortable, he takes off his trousers and puts on a dressing gown. But when a woman wants to be comfortable she slips into a pair of pants.

Pants are also our best friend when it comes to our weight. They tell us instantly when we have put on a few pounds by squeezing our stomachs and making sitting less pleasant. Listen to your pants. Don't buy a bigger size; lose the few extra pounds now.

8

Dressing Seductively in the Evening

Since most evening activities involve a favourite man – whether you dine by candlelight, visit friends, or go to the theatre – it's a time when you can be seductive and even provocative. You can pull out all the stops and use all the tricks to make yourself as pretty as possible. (If not now, when and where?)

Dressing for an evening out gives you a chance to escape from the realities of everyday life. You can give in to your fantasies by wearing a low neckline without feeling inhibited. Or you can have a slit in your skirt to show off your terrific legs. It's a time to relax and enjoy the admiration of your partner by being truly feminine for a few hours.

People often say that evening clothes allow you to become a different woman. That always makes me wonder why anybody would *want* to be a different person. I don't think it's possible or desirable. It's not possible, because if you're the type that wears tailored clothes in the daytime, it will be difficult for you to become a vamp at night. (You *can* become more glamorous and feminine by changing from a blazer and pants into a soft jersey dress that allows you to relax.) And it's not desirable because your man wants *you*. Spending an evening with a recognisable but seductive and

The luxurious fabric is what makes this simple blouse and pants sensual and outstanding.

desirable woman will be more exciting for him than wasting half the night getting used to a totally new look. So aim for glamour and even be daring, but stay yourself.

To help you decide what to wear, think of what you're going to do. If you go dancing, wear a pair of comfortable shoes and a flowing dress, not something that makes movement difficult. If you visit a friend's place where everyone sits on the floor, wear a pair of pants so you will feel like part of the group. If you're in doubt about how to dress and you can't find out from your host or your partner, stay simple; a nice silk dress, a black skirt and blouse, a suit with an evening sweater. Nothing is more embarrassing than being overdressed. Underdressing can always mean that you didn't know, but overdressing spells bad taste.

Also think of temperature changes. A restaurant may be warmer than the theatre (although air conditioning may make it frigid in summer). It's hard to have a good time when you feel too cold or too hot. Be sure to wear something that can be adjusted such as a wrap or a jacket.

NOTE

135

To get an evening off to a good start think of how your partner will dress. If you know him well, you'll have an idea. But if it's your first date, dress simply; you won't embarrass him by looking too good. Yes, that is possible. Many men are intimidated by an over-dressed or too-elegant woman. It scares them. I heard one man say: 'You should have seen how Laura was dressed. I wonder where she thought I was taking her.' So try to be feminine but not too dressed up.

Today the difference between styles for day and those for night has become very small. The basic pieces – pants, dresses, blouses – are the same. The distinction is made by the fabrics. You can find the same classic jumpsuit in a wool fabric for day and in gold lame for evening. A long T-shirt dress can become an evening dress when made in a silky material.

EVENING FABRICS

Silk, crepe de chine, silk satin, lamé, georgette, organza, chiffon, velvet, and taffeta can all be found in dresses, blouses, suits, pants, and tunics. Most of these, with the exception of velvet and some heavy silk satins, are year-round fabrics. Remember, any material that shines or glitters has a special appeal. Some fabrics have a hint of glitter, others really shine and sparkle. Which is for you depends not only on the occasion but also on your figure. A lot of shine is only for a SLIM WOMAN because it does make one look bigger; in other words, the amount of shine should decrease with the number of pounds.

EVENING COLOURS

The first colour that comes to mind for evening is black. It is exciting, mysterious, and always appropriate. But, as I have said, it must either show skin somewhere or be worn with a touch of a lighter or brighter colour or with jewellry. White is luxurious and flattering to a woman's face. But evening is also the time when you can get away from the basic beiges and greys, when you can think of vibrant colours like turquoise, emerald green, orange, red, steel blue, and shocking pink.

Before we actually proceed to dress for the evening I would like to remind you again of how important sexy underwear is. As I said in Chapter 2, it can add to the excitement of a wonderful evening.

BASIC WARDROBE FOR EVENING

In order not to worry about what to wear and to be seductive, you need to plan your evening wardrobe as carefully as the one for day. I have already mentioned several adaptable items that can be worn for both day and evening. Here is a list of eleven items (including a suit and white blouse suitable for day) that will give you an extensive choice!

- black suit
- simple black dress in jersey, wool, or silk (or any solid colour in a classic style)
- black pants
- vibrant-colour blouse

- white blouse
- evening sweater
- angora sweater
- camisole or halter
- tunic
- sequin or velvet jacket
- feather boa

Here are some ways you can combine these items to multiply your total of evening looks:

Black suit worn with
- vibrant-colour blouse
- white blouse
- evening sweater
- camisole or halter

Skirt of suit alone with
- camisole, sequin, or velvet jacket
  =5 looks

Black dress
- by itself with accessories
- sequin or velvet jacket
- feather boa
  = 3 looks

Black pants worn with
- vibrant-colour blouse
- camisole and sequin or velvet jacket
- evening sweater
- angora sweater
- tunic
- white blouse and sequin or velvet jacket
  = 6 looks

This gives you 14 different looks.

This list does not include cocktail dresses or long gowns; they will be discussed separately. The items suggested above would be suitable for a variety of occasions: dining in a restaurant with business associates or friends (in the suit or dress), an evening in a disco (in pants and a camisole), or a party at your boss's home (in pants, a white blouse, and a sequin jacket). Most of these items are year-round garments. You might want to substitute a white suit for a black one and a silky knit top for the angora sweater in the summer.

Except for basic items like your pants or the black dress, it isn't wise to spend a lot of money on clothes for evening. They don't have to stand up to a lot of wear and tear as they are worn only occasionally. When I ask women how much they would spend on a dress for daytime and how much for an evening outfit, they always answer that they would pay more for evening wear. Logically, it should be the other way around. Your daytime clothes are the ones that have to be of good quality because you wear them more.

NOTE

If you want to add something to this list, I suggest you increase the number of tops you wear with your pants, or buy another dress. A jumpsuit would also be a good idea, maybe a strapless one. This way you can wear it outside your home with a jacket or silk shirt and by itself for evenings at home.

DETAILS

The clothes you wear in the evening must suit and fit you well, but you can influence their effectiveness through a number of details.

Your Hair

Let it down. Never gather it into a chignon or pull it away from your face, because this will look severe. The looser and wilder your hair falls, the more seductive it will be. For business evenings you might want to be a little more moderate, but keep the look soft and pretty.

Your Make-up

Even if you don't wear much or any make-up during the day, it's a must in the evening. The soft lights in a restaurant or nightclub will wash out your features. Your eyes will have no expression. (And you know, of course, that the most effective instrument for seduction are the eyes.) So wear a good, more intensified eye make-up. If you don't know how to do it, take a make-up lesson and have an expert show you once. If you already wear make-up, just remember that for evening you have to apply more of everything, especially eye make-up.

Perfume

Like invisible arms, the scent of your perfume reaches out and says to someone 'I am here!' Not only will your perfume affect others, it will also influence how sensual you feel. Another advantage of your scent is that it's still there when you're gone – on his clothes, in his car, or on his pillow.

Tights

For evening, wear extra-sheer tights, the type that shines and makes noise when you cross your legs. Let the colour be as natural and close to your skin as possible (unless your outfit demands a special colour). The alternative – and a very sexy one – is to wear stockings and a garter belt. (Remember what I said in the lingerie chapter?)

Shoes

A sexy evening shoe must be high-heeled (as high as possible). It could be a sling back or for a still sexier look a high-heeled sandal. Assuming that you have co-ordinated the colours of your evening clothes, two pairs should be enough. One could be black or burgundy (a very easy colour to coordinate), or whatever colour fits best with your wardrobe. The other pair could be gold or silver sandals. Don't think that gold or silver has to be reserved only for big occasions. Even for a dinner a gold sandal with a black dress can look very appropriate.

If cold weather prevents you from wearing open shoes outside, let me tell you how Canadian women (who endure long, cold winters) solve the problem. The first time I went to a restaurant in Montreal, it was bitter cold and there were three feet of snow on the ground. What else could I wear but my boots? As I clumped into the restaurant, I wondered what the three women arriving at the same time had in their little cloth bags. Then each one, after removing her coat, pulled out a pair of elegant shoes. As a matter of fact, there was a whole assortment of boots in the cloakroom. I regretted that I had no bag of my own. The motto is: 'When there's a will, there's a way.'

Evening Bags

Don't worry too much about your bag because it's the item that is seen the least. Usually it goes onto a seat or under the table. Even when you carry it, it's not very prominent. So buy simple styles in good quality that you can use for many years.

I suggest one envelope bag that matches your dark shoes. Get it with a gold chain that can be hidden inside. When wearing a dress, carry the bag as a clutch; when wearing pants, use the gold chain to sling it over your shoulder. This type of bag is suitable for afternoon, too. The other bag should be a small evening bag to match your sandals. But don't get it too tiny. It should hold at least your comb, lipstick, powder, keys, and money.

Glittering Stones

Nothing is prettier than glitter in soft light. The stones that sparkle the most are diamonds. But a lot of us don't own them – or are afraid to wear them. So imitations can be just as successful. Dangling rhinestone earrings look smashing with a big scooped neckline. If the evening doesn't call for much glitter, make sure that the gold jewellry you wear is shiny, not dull. Keep in mind that anything glittering gives vivacity to your face.

A Feather Boa

You can look as glamorous with a feather boa as the woman in *Harper's Bazaar* – don't think it's not for you.

A boa can dress up any simple garment such as your simple black dress or a plain tunic worn with pants. Choose a colour like black, white, or bottle green (you will be surprised at how easy this shade is to coordinate). Colours like blue, pink, or yellow are too show-biz. If at first you feel uneasy wearing it around your neck, carry it over your arm; even there it will do something for your total look.

NOTE | Instead of buying a boa in a department store, check out your accessory store first. Stores selling trimmings usually carry boa feathers by the yard. You can choose the length you want, and it will be cheaper.

Your Back

This is not a detail you can buy, but it is a part of you that should be considered more often. Think about it: this is one part of the body that all women can show without feeling exposed or obvious. It doesn't matter whether you're slim or heavy, tall or small – your back always looks good. A low-cut back never fails to carry a sensual implication. If you've never made use of that part of your body, think about it seriously the next time you dress for evening.

142

COCKTAIL DRESSES

This term describes a short evening gown worn for dinner dances or special parties. The skirt is important. It should flow and move easily with your body. Avoid heavy, stiff fabrics; chiffon, silk, and jersey are best. A skirt with an uneven hemline or a style that's short in the front and trailing in the back is not very sexy-looking. The most becoming style for a cocktail dress is one that has a full, swinging skirt. How much fabric is suitable for you depends on the size of your hips and on your height. For a SLIM WOMAN a ful skirt pulled in at the waist will be graceful. For a HEAVY WOMAN a straight tunic over a skirt would be more becoming.

Chiffon is especially attractive for a short evening gown. As you can see in the picture, the skin that can be seen indirectly gives the dress a sensual feeling in spite of the long sleeves and the rather covered-up look. As far as styles that would look good on *you*, remember the guidelines in the chapter on dresses (including the length).

LONG DRESSES

Isn't it a treat to wear a long dress? Unfortunately, most of us rarely have an occasion to do so, except for maybe an annual dinner dance or an evening wedding. One piece of advice: whether you wear a long dress often or rarely, you should never buy one in advance – even though it is on sale! Of course everybody loves a bargain, and seeing a long dress reduced from £200 to £70 is tempting. But it's not a good buy if you don't know when you will need it. If you're invited ten months later to a dance, you'll feel obliged to wear it, even if you don't like it much anymore, because it has been hanging in your closet for months. Don't let a bargain spoil your fun. Buy a long dress just before you need it. Nothing gives you a greater lift than wearing something brand new. But to avoid feeling self-conscious, wear it for an evening at home first. If you get the feeling of it, you'll appear at ease and relaxed. Have you ever noticed how some women look stiff in an evening gown? It seems as if they don't dare move or even know how to. Obviously, this distracts from a sensual image.

NOTE | If you're lucky, you can find a long gown that will lend itself to being cut and hemmed later on to a cocktail style. This is not always possible, however, so it shouldn't be the deciding factor when you're buying a long dress.

STRAPLESS DRESSES

Wearing a strapless dress depends on how comfortable you feel in one and how good your figure looks in it. You will probably conclude that one has to be slim – true. But if her collarbones stick out or her arms aren't firm, even a slim woman won't look attractive in a strapless gown. It is becoming only when it exposes something pretty.

If you buy a dress like this, try to get one that comes with a shawl or stole, preferably in the same material. You won't be wearing your wrap or jacket inside and it might be chilly. Also you might feel better if you have a chance to cover yourself a little. If you're looking at dresses that have no cover-ups, and you don't have a suitable one at home, reconsider buying the dress. Stoles and shawls in soft, flowing fabrics can be a solution.

ONE-SHOULDER STYLES

Although a rather bare design, this is very elegant and more discreet than a strapless style. To be sensual it has to be a soft material that moulds the body, and preferably long. A short version does not give a sensual feeling. Since it exposes less than a strapless style, the one-shoulder dress could be an alternative for the woman who doesn't want to feel so undressed. For a SLIM WOMAN it looks good worn with a belt; for a HEAVY WOMAN it is a flattering style when straight.

For evening gowns you can use the richest fabrics and the most elaborate decorations such as ribbons, flowers, and jewellry. Dark silks and taffetas (which make a charming noise when you walk) are very becoming when worn with light trimmings or glittering gems. The style of a dress for a gala evening can be dressy and since evenings like this come seldom, you should choose the most out-standing but flattering style you can find. Forget about being prac-tical and economical. Splurge and don't think of how often you can wear this dress. If it is for a once-a-year event, you certainly don't want to wear it again next year. There are times that come but once, and so should the things that belong to it.

NOTE	Whenever you show a lot of skin – arms, neckline, back – extend your make-up to cover it with a frosted powder (which, of course, you will be using on your face, too). It gives a beautiful glow to your skin.

To enjoy your evening out, it is most important to feel comfort-able with yourself. Follow your own feelings rather than what someone else says. If you feel better in a silk dress than in a camisole, by all means wear it. But ask yourself whether sticking to the silk dress could indicate a lack of courage or adventurousness. Maybe if you think about it, you will be game enough to wear a low-cut dress the next time. Social evenings should make you for-get your work, your daily worries, your obligations – you should enjoy being a woman.

In closing this chapter let me tell you what happened to me a few years ago. I had a date with a man I didn't know well, so I asked him what I should wear. His answer surprised me and put me on the spot. 'Well,' he said, 'wear something that will be appropriate in a bar, a restaurant, the theatre, a nightclub, and . . . for breakfast.'

9

Sexy
Clothes
to
Wear
at Home

When it comes to looking good at home the first and most important rule is: DON'T WEAR YOUR OLD CLOTHES AROUND THE HOUSE. Being at home doesn't mean that you're constantly doing dirty work. You might clean thoroughly once or twice a week – and then by all means wear that old pair of pants and the worn top you've kept for the purpose. But once you've finished, change into something becoming.

   Your home is also the place where you can wear fashion fads that you aren't able to wear for work or outside your home (provided they suit you). Relaxing in a velour top that's inappropriate for the office or at a luncheon will make you feel 'with it' and less of a slave to the conventions you might follow in everyday life.

I've asked many women why they don't wear nice clothes at home. Their excuses are numerous: 'Nobody sees me'; 'I don't want to ruin my good clothes'; 'I want to be comfortable.'

While doing a wardrobe consultation for one of my clients, we weeded out a number of outfits that she didn't look attractive in anymore. Every time we put something aside, she said, 'Well, I'll keep it for cleaning the house.' After we had a large pile of clothing classified that way, I asked her how often she cleaned. She looked at me in puzzlement and then laughed. 'You're right,' she said, 'I only clean once a week.' Moral of the story: don't keep all your old clothes; two or three items are usually enough for this purpose.

The 'Nobody sees me' excuse is the poorest of all, because it is the most damaging to your confidence. Your old clothes don't flatter you, so every time you pass a mirror you'll see an image you don't like. Even if you're not consciously thinking about it, this negative image affects you. You won't be happy or sure of yourself and might even feel depressed. You should always be dressed so that you're not afraid when the doorbell rings unexpectedly. If you're on your way to the laundry in the basement, you don't want to be embarrassed when you meet the good-looking man from the tenth floor.

The 'I don't want to ruin my good clothes' excuse is acceptable only when you're talking about your Sunday best. Surely you have nice pants and tops that will not be ruined if you wear them while relaxing.

The 'I want to be comfortable' response isn't a very good excuse either.

There's no reason why you can't look good and be at ease at the same time. Isn't a pyjama-type outfit or a jumpsuit just as comfortable as baggy old jeans?

If you're married, your husband's impression of you is at stake. Evenings and weekends are probably the only times you're together. All your excuses for not wearing better clothes or looking good won't help you when he (unwittingly, of course – at least at first) compares you with the women he has seen during the day. They probably don't look better than you when they're at home, but your husband doesn't see them like that. Make an effort to look feminine for him. You can use this time to outshine the women he deals with in his professional life. They can't afford to be as sexy-looking as you can be at home, so don't let this chance go by.

Take a look at your wardrobe and get rid of the old clothes you've been hanging around in. If they're gone they won't tempt you again in the future. This includes the comfortable, frayed, discoloured bathrobe you've had for years. You can feel just as comfortable in a new one and you'll look a lot better.

For the working woman the best way to relax at home is to wear clothes that are the opposite of what she wears during the day. If you wear suits and dresses all day, a pair of pants will give you a more casual feeling. If you spend the day in pants, the looseness of a skirt or dress will make you feel more at ease. This advice also applies to women who stay at home. If you wear pants while doing errands and working around the house, a soft caftan will make you feel more feminine in the evening.

The at-home wardrobe can be divided into three categories: (1) clothes for daywear and relaxing; (2) tête-à-tête clothes, and (3) clothes for entertaining.

CLOTHES FOR DAYWEAR AND RELAXING

Jumpsuits

A jumpsuit (not to be confused with an overall) has sleeves and is either zipped or buttoned up the front. You can also find it without sleeves for the summer, or even strapless. The legs can be straight or pulled in with elastic at the ankles. The most practical type is the plainest style possible, with a straight leg. Since you will be wearing

it around the house, try to avoid a very light shade that would need frequent cleaning or washing; a dark colour or a soft print is preferable.

The advantage of the jumpsuit is that it is casual and comfortable yet suitable for unexpected visitors or errands.

Many women think that they can't wear a jumpsuit because it's good only for TALL SLIM WOMEN. This is not so. A SMALL SLIM WOMAN will look taller in one. But she should stick to straight legs – no harem pants, flared trousers, or cuffs. A SMALL HEAVY WOMAN can consider a jumpsuit if it's in a subdued colour, beltless and plain, and not too snug. A TALL SLIM WOMAN will look sexy, long-legged, and taller in a jumpsuit. She can afford to try all the fantasies available. A TALL HEAVY WOMAN can profit from this one-piece look because it will give her a more uniform shape. But it should be a little on the loose side, without a belt. A model with a zipper up the front is better than one with buttons.

Jeans and Pants

This is the one item of clothing that is worn most often at home. It is also the item that is greatly influenced by what you wear with it. Pants can look sporty, sexy, seductive, bulky, casual, dressed-up, and awful.

NOTE | Women who feel that jeans or pants are not suitable for their age should reconsider. It is not the pants themselves that make the difference but what is worn with them. Your daughter might wear pants and jeans with a halter top or a tight T-shirt. If you wear them with a nice blouse and a belt, they will look as good on you as they do on her.

Tops

The sex appeal of jeans and pants depends a lot on the top. The choice is vast. The most natural is the shirt. A cotton one (or cotton and polyester mix) would be most appropriate for daytime. To look sexy tuck it into your jeans or pants and always wear a belt. You can also tie the bottom of the shirt at your waist

An exception to this rule should be made by the HEAVY WOMAN. She should wear her tops on the outside of her pants.

Speaking of shirts, you might want to consider your husband's shirts as extra tops – even those he wears to the office. Once my husband stops wearing a shirt, I try it on and often keep on wearing it long after he has discarded it. Since he is bigger than I (as is the case with most husbands), his shirts are loose, but that just adds sex appeal, provided I wear them a certain way. I roll up the sleeves to a good length (either just below the elbow or three inches above), leave some buttons open, and stand up the collar. Seeing it like that on me makes him want his shirt back – but now it's too late.

Other tops to wear with jeans or pants are:

	• These look good only on women without bulges. Even a size 8 can have a spare tire.
T-shirts	• Bulky loose styles that reach the top of the thighs.
Sweaters	
Amusing styles	• For instance, a sweater with a tiger head extending down the sleeves, or oversized turtlenecks.
Velour tops	
Halters	
Bandeaus	• Made in rich colours, with a V-neck.
	• As is in summer; in winter, worn with an open shirt.
	• The style that exposes the midriff is good on non-bulging figures. (Most men regard a bare midriff as very sexy.)

Vests

The vest has many functions and purposes. It can make a simple shirt and pair of pants look more interesting, and it also keeps the torso warm. To be more striking, vests should always be made of a fabric that is different from the rest of your outfit – maybe in patchwork, in a loose weave, or fringed.

Besides the interest a vest can add to your overall look, it is also extremely practical for wearing at home. It leaves your arms free for work around the house. A SMALL SLIM WOMAN should wear only a short vest, to her waist or just slightly longer. She can afford to have it fitted. A MEDIUM-TALL SLIM WOMAN can wear a tight vest as well as a loose one, and a long style as well as a short one. A fitted vest that ends at the waist will make her legs appear longer. A MEDIUM-TO-TALL HEAVY WOMAN should wear only loose vests, but whether she is SLIM or HEAVY, these can be any length. Just above the knee is a length that is slimming for a larger woman.

You may be thinking that it's hard to find interesting vests and if you do they're expensive. True on both counts. The reason is that making a vest requires more work than most people think. I've heard many women say that they don't want to pay 'that much' for a sleeveless garment. But if you think how versatile it is and how it can change many otherwise dull outfits you might feel more willing to spend the money.

Skirts

If you wear mostly pants or jeans at home, changing into a skirt can make you feel more feminine. I'm not talking about ordinary skirts here – at home you can wear a fuller, longer skirt. It might be made from a gauzy print in the summer and a soft wool in the winter, in a solid colour or a print. Ethnic looks – Indian prints, for example – are great for skirts to wear at home.

Shorts

For summer, shorts can be sensual-looking. But be sure your legs still look as good in them as they used to. Are your thighs slim? If you have the smallest bulge on either the outside or inside of the leg, you'll look better in jeans. For shorts to be sexy, they have to be as short as possible with slits at the sides. Never consider a boy-leg cut, or worse yet, Bermuda shorts. Shorts worn with a blouse

look more interesting than with a halter or bandeau; the exposure the shorts provide is quite enough.

Warm-up Suits

You don't have to be a jogger to wear a warm-up suit. These are not only pretty but super comfortable. The fabrics vary from cotton sweatshirt material to soft velour. The most practical design available is the one with a zipper up the front, because you can leave it open to exactly where you want it. Also, since it's a simple design, you won't get tired of it.

I suggest a darker colour to avoid frequent washing. A light colour loses its fresh look after one wearing, even if it's not actually dirty. And for 100-percent cotton or velour, frequent washing does not improve the look.

Peasant Dresses

If your style is conservative and classic during the day, you might find a peasant dress a relaxing change at home. The styles vary from a very full look worn with a belt (good for a SLIM WOMAN) to a less-ample design worn without a belt (good for a HEAVY WOMAN). Long sleeves are more attractive than short sleeves.

If the dress has a ribbon through the top, change it to an elastic. This will allow you to pull it off your shoulders. Made from gauzy, silky fabrics or fine cotton (for summer) and wool or jersey (for winter), this is a very becoming design, in the short or long version.

NOTE	The SMALL WOMAN has to be very careful that a dress of this type is not too long. If it is, she will look squat and dumpy.

TÊTE-À-TÊTE CLOTHES

Twosome occasions give you a chance to be more daring (consider styles that you wouldn't otherwise have an opportunity to wear). And don't think your man won't like your wearing a transparent shirt. If you wear it just for him, he won't mind – in fact, he'll probably welcome it. I know a woman who got very upset when her husband gave her a glittering low-cut dress as a joke – the kind of dress nightclub performers wear. It seemed to me he was telling her he wanted her to be more provocative. So if you ever receive a present like this (seriously or not), instead of being offended try to see if someone is sending you a message.

If you aren't married and you plan a candlelight dinner with a man you don't know well, don't overdo it. He could get scared if he finds you in a slinky gown when he arrives in jeans. But once you know the man, married to him or not, be more adventurous (not only with your clothes).

Should the children or other circumstances not allow for a tête-à-tête dinner, create them. Go away for a weekend or send the children to their grandparents for an evening. For a good relationship you need some moments alone, time for each of you to give the other some undivided attention. During those precious moments, your clothes can help to create fantasies that are in a different world from your everyday life – how far away you want to go from everyday events only you can decide. Here are some ideas to get you started:

- Don't choose a style that is difficult to get out of; you don't want to be caught fumbling, do you? Pick fabrics that mould and show your body, such as jersey or knits. This is a more sensual approach than a plunging neckline.

155

- Wear high-heeled, open sandals. Stay out of slippers; they aren't sexy.

NOTE

> This is true regardless of the outfit you wear or the time of day: If you want to look good at home, avoid clogs and old slippers.

Bodystockings

The style with legs and feet and long sleeves looks good worn by itself or with a short skirt over it. Also sensual are designs with a scoop neck, tank top, or low-cut back; any of these looks good with a wraparound skirt or a large scarf tied over your hips.

If you can't find a really big scarf, use a large square piece of fabric. You can also wear it over a plain outfit (for instance, a pair of black evening pants and a sweater) or by itself (tied above the bust) so that it becomes a short dress. This kind of scarf should be in a lively design and bright colours.

Kimonos

A kimono is flattering and becoming to ANY FIGURE TYPE, tall or short, large or small, and can be worn at any age. The short or three-quarter version can replace a tunic. They are as handy and comfortable as dressing gowns, but don't look like one. (They are also easy to get out of.) In rich fabrics with high side slits they are a feminine evening look. Kimonos are also worn by men. If your husband has one, you may be able to share it with him!

Other Tops

If you wear your lace blouse with a camisole when dining out for a *rendezvous à deux* at home, wear it without anything underneath. The same applies to any transparent garment you own. You could call it teasing, but then there is no man who minds being teased a little – as long as you deliver. If you dare, you can even wear a dress that way.

A tunic worn over a pair of evening pants or, better yet, alone gives an elegant look. It is emphasised if the fabric is soft and there are slits on either side.

156

Caftans

A caftan is one of the most comfortable garments for leisure wear. It is a style that allows you to wear a garter belt underneath . . . or nothing at all. However, to look sexy, it should always fall loosely and flow when you move. A SMALL WOMAN, SLIM or HEAVY, must stick to solid colours; a print will drown her figure line. A MEDIUM-TO-SLIM WOMAN will look good in all colours and in subtle prints. A MEDIUM-TO-TALL HEAVY WOMAN must be careful that the caftan is not cut so large that it makes her look square. HEAVY WOMEN often think that draping more material around them will hide them. Not so. They will just look bigger than they actually are.

Short Little Dresses

If you have nice legs use them by wearing a mini-type skirt or dress. Legs have a great sensual impact. You can also wear a longish tunic that will look like a dress if you belt it; blouse the top slightly.

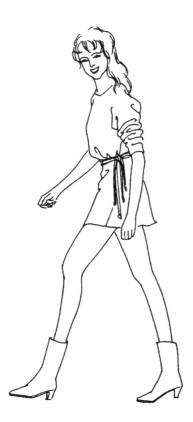

High-heeled sandals are terrific with this type of look. Or you can wear boots to increase the sexual emphasis even further.

I'm sure that once you see the role your clothes can play in pleasurable evenings alone with a man, you will come up with ideas I haven't even thought of.

CLOTHES FOR ENTERTAINING

The reason we change into something pretty when receiving guests is not only to look good but to honour our visitors, to tell them that they are important to us. But don't dress up more than your guests, or you will embarrass them. (You can avoid this by describing the occasion clearly when you offer an invitation.)

What to wear depends on how important the guests are. For a dinner with friends a pair of jeans and a pretty blouse will be enough, but if you give a New Year's party a long dress is fitting. Keep in mind that for home entertainment you can pick styles that would not be fitting for streetwear.

Unusual Tops

The evening pants I suggested for your wardrobe in the previous chapter can also be worn at home with different tops: a Chinese satin jacket, a sequin halter, a hand-loomed shirt, and so on. If you entertain a lot you will need more than one pair of pants. Chocolate-brown, grey satin, even gold lamé pants all look wonderful worn with a simple shirt.

Pyjamas

Hostess pyjamas have to be chosen carefully in order not to look like sleeping pyjamas, especially if they're made in soft fabrics like jersey. This type of outfit can be worn by ALL FIGURE TYPES, but do remember what I've said about suitability when it comes to styles. Bold prints are for a TALL SLIM WOMAN only. Solids are better for SMALL and HEAVY WOMEN. This is a perfect at-home look, but don't wear it out – especially not to a restaurant or dinner dance.

Long Skirts

For a special party or a black-tie dinner at your home, an ankle-length skirt with a white blouse always looks festive and feminine. Although this length is less dressed-up for a hostess than a floor-length skirt, it's a little sexier, as it exposes part of the leg.

For a floor-length skirt to be attractive, length alone is not the key. A long straight skirt can be lifeless unless the cut, fabric, or details make it interesting. I have often heard people say, 'She wore just a long skirt and a blouse' – rather a dull description, wouldn't you say? Do look for diverse items and different styles that get away from run-of-the-mill looks.

Whatever you decide to wear at home, keep in mind that:
• You should feel good about yourself.
• You should be able to open the door at any time without feeling embarrassed about your looks.
• You should, when around your man, dress as if you were ready to make love or, if the time and circumstances don't allow it, as if you would like to.

10
The Sensual
Sleeper

Because sleeping isn't the only thing we do in bed, women should consider nightclothes as tantalising appetisers. A nightgown should show enough skin to arouse interest, but hide enough to keep the mystery. How can you appear mysterious after many years of marriage or a long relationship? The right nightgown can, indeed, be the needed ingredient.

In the privacy of your own home you can afford to be less lady-like. A nightgown can help you look sexy or even erotic. But because nightclothes are more exposing than other garments, you have to pay special attention to your assets, the areas you want to show most. Firm breasts can afford minimal coverage or transparent fabrics. Nice legs can be shown to their best advantage in short styles or through long slits. And exposed shoulders are a most attractive feature, one that every woman can show regardless of her figure.

Evidence suggests that until the sixteenth century, most people slept naked. By about 1800 daytime smocks and shirts were worn for sleeping. Only in the nineteenth century did nightclothes acquire an identity of their own. Women wore long gowns made of white cotton, at times decorated with lace or embroidered. But the nightgown did not become glamorous until the 1880s, when women's underwear became more luxurious too.

There are indications that in the eighteenth century nightgowns were also worn as evening dresses. Today, too, there are designs that look very much like dresses – so much so that in recent years some women have worn night gowns as dresses at home or even outside the house.

This leads to the question of fit. A nightgown should fit as well as anything else. The extra comfort you're looking for doesn't justify a fitted bodice to be loose. Don't think: 'It's just a nightdress.' You're seen in it when you go to bed and when you get up – both important moments.

NOTE | When buying nightwear, try on garments to make sure they suit you and fit well. Many times I've like a style on a hanger, but not on me. You might wonder what could be wrong with a loose style that has long sleeves and pretty lace trimming. A lot. The shoulders might not be where your shoulders are. Or the sleeves might be too short. Don't take a risk; check it out.

If you are on your own, you may feel that it's not necessary to pay attention to your nightwear. But wearing something unattractive to sleep in will not improve the reflection you see in the mirror. Like wearing old clothes at home, it's detrimental to your self-confidence. Remember, it's just as important to look good for yourself as for others.

DETAILS TO HELP YOU LOOK BETTER AND FEEL MORE
COMFORTABLE

• A long nightgown should be long. One that it too short for you will detract from your sensual image.
• Your bust must be where the style of the gown intends it to be. An empire style, for example, is made to cup just below the bust; if a

gown like this doesn't fit you in the right place, look for another style.

- Wear designs that are easy to undo and get out of. It is embarrassing to end up with your nightgown around your waist or under your arms. If your local stores don't carry the right designs, wear a robe instead, or order from a mail order company (most advertise in fashion magazines).
- Choose fabrics that have a sheen, are soft to the touch, and don't cling. Silk satin is the most luxurious but also the most difficult to care for. Good alternatives include polyester satin charmeuse and

Most fabrics today call for machine washing, but if you want them to last longer and look prettier, wash them by hand and dry them *on a hanger*. | **NOTE**

anti-cling tricot. Flowery fabrics are nice for summer looks.

- Slippers make a big difference. The ultimate chic is to match them to the colour of your gown. But that would require having as many pairs of slippers as gowns – an investment few of us can afford. So I suggest as an alternative that you match your slippers to the colour of your robe or buy a gold on silver look. They should always have a little heel; flats are not very flattering.
  - Cut-outs and slits add a sensual note. They can be on the side, the front, or the back; choose the one that exposes what you want to show. The style in the illustration on the previous page is good for a woman with a MEDIUM-SIZE BUST.
  - Lace trimmings always make nightclothes more beautiful. A delicate combination is to have the lace in a different colour from the fabric.
  - As to colour, consider shades you've never worn before, some thing different from the habitual pinks and light blues. Many women associate black nightgowns with shady lifestyles, but that's really a myth. You, too, can wear one. The contrast that black creates with any skin colour is most exciting.

TYPES OF NIGHTCLOTHES

Before speaking about becoming styles, let me point out which ones are not. At the top of the list of unsexy designs is the flannel night-gown; the style is never sensual and even the fabric alone makes the wearer appear matronly.

Also avoid anything that is completely closed up to the neck. The unreachable look is not appealing. A neither-here-nor-there style is the short nightgown or sleepshirt that ends above the knee. It makes the legs look as if they're dangling from nowhere.

Flattering Styles

One man described the ideal nightgown this way: 'It should either be a short, flimsy one to fool around in or a long, elegant one that makes the imagination run away.' In other words, be overtly sexy or tormentingly seductive. Fortunately, there are many styles that fall in either category.

A sexy gown should always expose the neck and shoulders.

What is most becoming for the rest of the figure is determined by the size of the bust.

These and similar models neither hide the bust nor expose it; instead the extra material adds volume.

For a SMALL BUST

- One-shoulder styles (p166, illustration No. 1)
- V-necks open to the waist, or to just below the bust with gathers coming from the shoulders (illustration No. 2)
- A bodice cut straight across the top of the breasts or as close to the nipples as comfortable, and held by thin straps (illustration No. 3)
- A bodice with lace around the top of the bust, held by straps, with the fabric falling straight down (illustration No. 4)

For a MEDIUM BUST

If your breasts are firm, you can wear any style at all:

- open to the waist (illustration No. 1)
- fitted at the bust and waist (illustration No. 2)
- transparent fabrics (illustration No. 3)

If your bust needs support, you are better off with a style that holds the breasts – such as illustration No. 4.

NOTE

Whether a gown falls loosely from the bust or is held in at the waist is a matter of personal preference. A fitted waist gives still more shape to the figure, but a loose style can also be sensual.

For a LARGE BUST

Because a large bust usually goes with a larger-size figure, this body type should never consider anything that is transparent.

Instead choose:

- loose styles with fullness coming from below the bust or from the shoulder (illustrations No. 1 and No. 4)
- gowns with long sleeves. If they have an elastic band at the wrist, make sure it is loose so that it doesn't cut into the flesh (illustration No. 1)
- open necklines, such as:
- a large boat neck (illustration No. 2)
- a deep V-neck (illustration No. 1)
- a low scoop neck (illustration No. 3)

As you can see, these styles give the impression of openness without showing much.

Baby-Dolls

The baby-doll is a cute and quite sexy look for a fairly slim woman. The complete exposure of the legs makes them appear slimmer, so don't dismiss this style, try one on. Follow the same guidelines for suitability as for a long gown. If you can't find a sexy style in your local store, try a mail-order house.

Winter Nightwear

Contrary to what you might think, it's possible to be beautiful and warm at the same time. Brushed nylon fabrics are soft and comfortable. But don't buy a style closed up to the neck. Try something like this:

Another way to be warm and sexy in winter is to wear a bed jacket. Some nightdresses come with a jacket. For others, it's easy to find knitted or cloth jackets. White is the most versatile colour, one that coordinates well with everything.

Pyjamas

Many women don't care for pyjamas, because they give a feeling of being confined. However, if you do wear them, they look younger and more sensual with short or rolled up sleeves. A longer jacket is also more flattering than one that shows the top of the pants when you move. In an unconventional design, pyjamas can be a sexy alternative to a nightgown.

Peignoir and Negligee Sets

It is an exquisite luxury to wear a matching gown and robe. Nevertheless, these sets are costly and their image is very bedroomy. Thus they are not designed for everyday wear. For a weekend away, such a set would be nice. But for the home stick with a dressing gown that is pretty and practical. Remember that when a garment is out of place, it loses its charm.

Robes

The principle that women look good in men's clothes is once more confirmed. The most popular and becoming robe style for women is the same design as for men: the classical shawl-collar style.

171

Because of its simplicity it is suitable for ANY FIGURE TYPE. The long collar will help a SMALL WOMAN appear taller and a HEAVY WOMAN look slimmer. For the latter, in fact, there is no style that is more becoming. It looks attractive in all kinds of fabrics. You can have it in a warm material in the winter, and in cotton, silk, or any other lightweight fabric in the summer. The look can be varied with interesting details: contrasting piping around the edges, a satin collar and cuffs, embroidery or scallops around the collar.

The second choice, not very different from the first, has a notch collar instead of a shawl collar. It is made from many different fabrics, but looks especially good in terry cloth.

This type of robe originated as something to put on after a bath or a swim, but it has since become a dressing gown. It has a young, sporty look. One caution: don't wear the same terry cloth for years and years. Regrettably, they loose their freshness rather quickly and they are not attractive when the colours are faded and threads are pulled. (For a HEAVY WOMAN terry cloth is not a good selection because it will make her appear bigger.)

The colour of a robe should never be too pale. Most of us look pale enough when we get up in the morning, so we shouldn't emphasise it with a beige or light blue robe. Good colours include strawberry, chocolate brown, and burgundy.

If a white dressing gown has always been your dream, buy it only if it is not the only robe you own. White shows soil and since you won't wash your robe after every wearing you'll end up wearing a greyish garment most of the time.

NOTE

Robes with a zipper up the front are very popular and practical. Many pretty designs are made that way. They look very neat and are suitable for most women, but they are especially becoming on a HEAVY WOMAN, who might look better in a beltless style. The advantage of the zipper is that you can close it low or high, depending on place and time.

A long kimono is an elegant robe. Because of the wide sleeves it is not quite as practical as the other classic designs. But as a second or third robe it's a good choice.

The kimono is very suitable for ALL FIGURE TYPES. Since the cut is the same for a man's and woman's kimono, check the men's department. You will find more interesting fabrics and lower prices.

Did you know that quilted styles, so popular among women for many years, are disliked by men because they look heavy and bulky? Check it out and ask your man. You'll probably change to a wraparound robe very quickly.

NOTE

No robe will look elegant if your nightie is showing, whether at the hem or at the neckline. To avoid this, take your nightgown off before putting on your robe. Not only will you look better, but, with less bulk, you'll feel more comfortable too.

Never forget that looking your best when going to sleep is as important as when you're awake.

11

The Appeal of Accessories

Accessories are sensual only when used sparingly. Too often a scarf, heavy jewellry, or the wrong shoes prevent a woman from looking her best. Accessories are basically decoration, and too many can be distracting.

Accessories look attractive when they contribute to your total look by completing or emphasising it. They can change it too – for example, from day to evening wear or from a dressy to sporty look. When used correctly an accessory can even become a personal trademark. Most women realise this, but still worry that they don't know how to accessorise their wardrobes. Choosing the accessories that work best for you can be difficult.

The first step in learning how to accessorise your wardrobe is to remember that the essential items like shoes, bags, and stockings are not only useful but they can add interest to your look. They can make a statement about your personality, or become your personal insignia. You probably know women who always wear beautiful shoes or unusual bags. They have chosen these essential items to enhance their look and to be their trademark. So you don't need roses in your hair, big cummerbunds, or scarves tied around your head to accessorise your wardrobe. You can do it with the essentials only.

Aside from these necessary items, however, there are many other accessories from which to choose. When deciding what you should wear, start with what you like to wear. I have found that most women are drawn to some items more than others. There are women (like myself) who will die for jewellery, while others long for scarves. Your preference for one item over another means that you feel comfortable with it. This is very important. You can carry off an exotic scarf when you feel great wearing it, but not if you have to fuss with it all day long. If you are one of those women who shy away from scarves for this reason don't wear this accessory.

There's no reason you have to wear all the accessories available. But don't reject the idea of a belt or any other item if you've never worn it. If you try it, you might find that it changes your look favourably.

What accessories are you wearing now? Does your ring, for instance, say anything at all? Or is it neither unusual nor outstanding, neither small nor big – in other words, insignificant? Are your earrings so small that they're invisible once your hair falls over them? Do you feel apologetic about your shoes? Think of accessories as articles that carry a message. You are trying to say something when you wear a green belt or red shoes. Say it. Don't let it be unclear. This might sound as if I'm advising you to wear big or bright accessories. Not really. What I am saying is to stay away from mediocre items.

They serve no purpose except to make you look mediocre too.

Once you feel at ease wearing a certain kind of accessory, try an item you've never worn before. If it makes you look and feel good, it's a plus, but if you don't feel a hundred-percent relaxed in it, you don't need it. However, while experimenting with a new item, don't let the unfamiliarity make you decide against wearing this accessory. Try to make it work. Fashion magazines can tell you how and with what an item is worn. Only after wearing something a few times can you decide whether it is for you.

NOTE

The unusual items – those that will say something about you might not be available in your local department store. To find that special belt your new dress needs, for example, you may have to check out an unfamiliar boutique or specialty shop.

Because accessories can make other garments look up to date (or out of style), they should follow fashion trends more closely than the rest of your wardrobe. This is true of some accessories more than others – for instance, for shoes but not for scarves. While discussing the various accessories – starting from the top and working down – I'll point out if and how fashion trends affect each item.

HATS

There was a time when a woman without a hat was not fully dressed. But while hats completed a woman's attire then, today they make many women feel overdressed.

Fedora   (No. 1)

Fur Hat   (No. 3)

Cartwheel   (No. 2)

Woollen Hat   (No. 4)

Most women reserve hats for special occasions if they wear them at all (except for knitted caps in the winter). This is regrettable because a hat is one of the most flattering things a woman can wear to complete an outfit. Our lifestyles may not be conducive to cartwheel hats, but a fedora with a moderate brim is suitable for almost all women and it could find a place in anyone's life, in felt for winter and in straw for summer. But to gain the extra effect a hat adds to an outfit, you have to pay the price of being courageous enough to wear it. A hat attracts attention. It can be a conversation piece, a compliment catcher, and a confidence builder, as well as making you look more interesting. The style that does this best is a hat with a brim that covers the face partially, throwing a shadow over your eyes and framing your face (illustration No. 1).

To look sensual, the brim of a hat should always extend a little beyond the nose. A narrower brim looks neither elegant nor chic.

General Hints for Suitability

- The width of a brim depends not only on facial features but also on height. A SMALL WOMAN risks looking like a mushroom with too wide a brim.
- Hats like pillboxes, turbans, or other small styles that sit on top of the head are not very sensual. They cover your hair, leaving the face rather naked and exposed.
- The smaller the hat, the fuller the figure will appear. The larger the hat, the slimmer the figure will look.
- A hat must be in proportion with the rest of the figure. A TALL WOMAN should never wear a small hat. Neither should a HEAVY WOMAN.
- If you have a long nose or protruding jawline, the brim of the hat should extend beyond them. A smaller brim or brimless style will emphasise these features.
- The crown of the hat should be slightly higher and larger than your head. It will add a little height, which is never bad, and prevent your hair from being flattened. If you want to wear a high crown to add height to your look, however, be careful; you can easily look top-heavy.

Whenever you are trying on a hat, make sure that you can see your whole figure. You can judge whether the proportions are right only by seeing the entire silhouette.   **NOTE**

If hats don't fit into your daily lifestyle, you don't have to do without them completely. Wear a hat for weekend or leisure occasions. The most becoming hat for anybody of any age (men as well as women) is the cowboy hat. It might give your weekend wardrobe the extra note you've been looking for.

In the summer you can wear a straw hat – maybe with a scarf tied around it – to the beach or to the country club.

Leisure times are often spent with a man, and yours will welcome the added appeal a hat gives you. His admiration will help you feel less self-conscious about wearing hats, and might even convince you to wear them on other occasions as well.

Knitted Caps

A lot of these look more like bathing caps than hats – which is what makes them so unbecoming. Fitting closely around the head, covering and hiding the hair completely, they expose the face and make it look naked and severe. It's no secret that any face looks softer and more sensual with hair framing it. If you're looking for warmth and have to cover your hair, wear something soft and flattering. Try one made from fluffy wool, one with a thick brim (that is, with the edge turned over several times), an oversized beret, or a softly knitted cap big enough to add volume to your head without flattening your hair (illustrations No. 3 and No. 4).

You can further enhance the look of a warm hat by the way you wear it. It will look softer if it's pulled over your forehead, nearly touching the brows. For other ideas look at how the models in fashion magazines wear their berets or other head coverings. If you like the look, try it on yourself.

> Too many times a wool hat doesn't match the scarf worn with it. This poor co-ordination won't improve your look. Buying a set may seem expensive because you're paying for two items at once. But a scarf and hat bought separately won't save you money – and they may look awful together.
> An even better idea is a hat-and-scarf set with matching gloves. The extra money you spend will be a good investment; you won't have to worry about co-ordinating these accessories all winter.

NOTE

If you are still in doubt about what type of hat to wear, I suggest that you try on a few different styles the next time you pass a store's hat counter. The reflection in the mirror may convince you that a hat can do something for you,

SUNGLASSES

Sunglasses add instant sex appeal and mystery to a woman's look by hiding her eyes. And of course they still fulfil their original purpose of protecting the eyes from sun and glare.

Choosing a Style

How appealing sunglasses are depends a lot on finding the right shape for your face. If your face is:

> Because sunglasses are an accessory that changes with fashion trends, you should buy a new pair each year. To make matters worse, you should avoid cheap ones. Cheaper glasses lack refined styling and finish, and they don't stand up to daily wear and tear. The lenses scratch so easily that you soon think you've had the glasses for years. Clean your sunglasses frequently. They should be shiny and sparkling. Dull lenses detract from their appeal.

NOTE

OVAL

• you can wear large glasses. If your features are delicate, choose thin frames; if they're strong, buy a heavier frame.

ROUND	• you can wear large frames of any sort.
SQUARE	• wear a softening frame with some roundness to it.
HEART-SHAPED	• a rectangular frame with thin rims is the most suitable.

NOTE To find a pair of sunglasses that make you feel attractive as well as comfortable, you may have to try on ten or fifteen different pairs. Don't be embarrassed or intimidated by the salesperson when you ask for the eleventh pair – you're the one who has to wear them. If you wear prescription glassses, you can find nice styles – and more careful fitting – at the optician's office. Even if you don't need a pre-scription you may find this personalised service worthwhile.

Important Tips

- Avoid patterns or fads like rhinestones or monograms. They become tedious, especially if you can afford only one pair a year.
- Avoid bright definite colours like red, white, or blue. Pick a darker frame or a shade that will easily coordinate with your clothes. I once watched a young woman struggling to find glasses to match her earrings. A bit fussy, maybe, but it's better to fuss than not to care at all.
- The tint of the lenses should coordinate with the frame.

This is not a becoming design.

- To look attractive, sunglasses should be on the large side because they have to be visible. It is best when they cover the eyebrows.
- Beware of styles that point downward. This style leads the eyes down. When it comes to the face, one's glance should always be led upward.
- Avoid glasses that are tinted unevenly – clear at the bottom and opaque only in the upper half. This particular design does not help any woman who has dark circles or bags under her eyes; it just makes them more visible. Glasses with uniformly tinted lenses are preferable.
- When you're not wearing sunglasses, place them on top of your head or hang them in your decolletage of your blouse rather than carrying them in your bag.

If you don't wear sunglasses because you don't find them a necessary and attractive accessory, think of their practical uses. Besides protecting your eyes from sun, glare, and wind, they hide your eyes when you're tired, when you didn't have time to put on your make-up, or when you don't want to be recognised the morning after.

SCARVES

How much a scarf contributes to a sensual image depends more on the wearer than on the accessory itself. Some women love to wear scarves and arrange them well; others find them a bother. A scarf can be worn just about anywhere: on the head, encircling the waist, at the hips, and of course around the neck.

Some women wear a scarf simply to improve their look. Unfortunately, seven times out of ten it doesn't do so. There are few outfits that need a scarf to make them look better – except for a plain turtleneck or a crew-neck sweater. A blouse or dress with a collar does not need this extra piece.

I'm not ruling out scarves completely, though. When co-ordinated well in style and colour, they can be pretty additions.

The first and most important rule is that a scarf must never be cheap. The idea that a little ten pounds scarf can save or improve a dress is a myth. But an expensive one can make a ten pounds dress look fabulous.

The reason is that the scarf gets all the attention and makes the dress appear secondary. So buy only silk, not acetate or synthetic fabrics. The reason so many women can't keep a scarf in place is not that they don't know how to wear it but usually because it's the wrong type of silk. A heavy, springy silk will never stay in place and should be used only in a scarf worn with a coat. In order to wear a scarf with ease buy the softest type of silk you can find. It will stay put once you have adjusted it. A good alternative to silk is chiffon, which is even more pliable and softer-looking.

NOTE | If you can't find an attractive chiffon scarf, you can always buy a yard of fabric (or two for an evening stole). Don't worry about hemming it. The sides, being selvage, need no attention. All you have to do at the ends is pull some threads until you have a small fringe.

Size may also be a problem. If you are trying to wear a 12-inch square around your neck, you will feel choked. Try a 24 or 36-inch square instead.

Prints Versus Solids

A print scarf should be worn only with a solid-colour garment. Pattern on pattern looks too busy.

A solid-colour scarf is easy to coordinate and looks elegant. Even when worn with a solid-colour dress, it doesn't lose any of its effect. Imagine a navy suit with a light turquoise scarf – this is certainly more striking than a busy multi-coloured one. A bright-coloured outfit can be toned down with a solid scarf. If you have trouble finding the shade you need, remember that you can always buy the fabric and make your own.

Who Can Wear Scarves?

For a SMALL WOMAN scarves are a tricky matter. They tend to overpower her and make her look smaller. If this figure type must wear a scarf, she should consider only the softest type of silk or chiffon and wear it only around the neck, never around the waist.

For a TALL SLIM WOMAN squares are the best choice. She can easily afford the extra bulk a scarf adds and she can wear it anywhere on her body.

For a HEAVY WOMAN the oblong type is the most flattering. Whether it is worn closely around the neck or tied V-neck style at the bust, the flowing ends always let her appear slimmer. However, it must be long enough that when tied it still reaches down to the waist. If not it will make her appear heavier.

Wearing a scarf around the head is a question not only of how well you can drape it but also of whether it suits you. A head scarf looks better on a woman with a dark complexion and strong features than on one who has a pale face and fragile features.

For the woman who rarely or never wears scarves but who always seem to receive them as gifts, I would suggest tying one around the handles of her handbag or briefcase. It adds a nice feminine touch.

BELTS

Belts influence the silhouette and can do a lot to enhance your image. I find it surprising that so many women fail to take advantage of them. Maybe they feel that their waists are too large, or perhaps they don't realise what a belt can do for them. If you are one of these women, let me point out that a belt can bring out the shape of your body, complete an ensemble, and change your look.

Shaping your body doesn't mean that you have to pull a belt in tightly. One that's loosely knotted to hang easily around your waist can give definition to your silhouette just by indicating that there is a waist.

A belt can complete an outfit that is otherwise plain. Let's say you have a straight knitted dress. Most women would dress it up with jewellry. But a chain or pendant will not make it look as outstanding as an interesting belt.

By changing your belt, you can avoid changing your whole outfit. A black dress worn with a self belt during the day can be adapted for evening with a silver leather belt. Black pants and a white shirt can be dressed down in the daytime with a black leather belt, and dressed up at night with a gold chain.

A belt can make a difference in defining your figure proportion. A SHORT-WAISTED WOMAN can make her torso look longer by matching the colour of her belt to her top. (Another way is to wear a belt so that it sits a little below the natural waist.) If you are LONG-WAISTED match the belt to your skirt or pants. **NOTE**

The most important part of a belt is the buckle. It's the most noticeable feature and also determines whether the accessory is sporty or dressy. A square silver design looks proper on a Western belt, while a small gold one is quite dressy.

Who can wear belts? Most women can. Even a HEAVY WOMAN should not dismiss the idea, though she should never wear a belt wider than one inch. A nice buckle that can be seen under a jacket adds an attractive extra touch. (Do you recall the suit shown in Chapter 7)

For women with smaller waists, the choice is a matter of taste and appropriateness. For an everyday look invest in good leather belts that match your clothes in a discreet manner. The best width here is one to one-and-a-half inches. If you wear wider styles, stay with soft crushed leather sashes, because they look more feminine.

NOTE Never pull any belt too tightly around your waist; it will look constrained and make your hips appear larger. This applies to ALL FIGURE TYPES, but especially so to a HEAVIER WOMAN.

Don't try to follow belt fashion trends and fancies all the way unless your waist is one of your assets. If it's not, stick to basic, classic designs.

JEWELLERY

Jewellery can add glamour and luxury to an otherwise conservative wardrobe.

The shine and sparkle subtly accentuate your personality: a gold chain falling into the décolletage of your sports blouse, a pendant dangling between your breasts, a pair of shiny button earrings lightening your face.

It's wonderful when you can afford real jewels, but as far as effect is concerned, good costume jewellery can do as well – except for watches and rings. A good watch, as a status symbol, will impress everyone who sees it, and it also serves you longer and more precisely. Costume jewellery rings will make you look cheap in every sense of the word; stay away from them unless you're going to a masquerade ball.

Advice frequently given is: 'Don't wear too much jewellery.' This is true if you wear too many different pieces – earrings, chains, bracelets, rings – at the same time. But wearing three or four chains (or more) without any other jewellery can look terrific. A group of bracelets looks good but not if you wear rings on the same hand. One will minimise the effect of the other.

Jewellery, a very personal and individual accessory, has to be chosen with great care. Just because a ring is beautiful doesn't mean it will suit your hand.

Likewise don't let the beautiful workmanship of a pendant influence you. It might be too large or intricate for you. Every piece of jewellery must be judged and considered on the person wearing it.

A general rule when buying jewellery is to avoid anything that looks ordinary. This applies as much to size as to design. If you want a pair of button earrings, don't settle for pinhead size; they should be visible. Don't buy dull gold; it will give the impression of trying not to be there. Mediocre jewellery doesn't look exciting, and if it's real it's not even an investment.

Earrings

A pair of earrings can give life and vitality to your face. Even if you wear no other jewellery, earrings are a must for completing a woman's look. They add softness to a very short and severe hairstyle.

Button and hoop types are the easiest to wear. They are always appropriate and complement most outfits. If your face is long, wear a round design, but if your face is round wear an oblong style (not a dangling one). Drop earrings should be worn only in the evening, and not by anyone with a long thin face or a short neck, because they will accentuate these features.

Necklaces

A necklace should flatter your neckline. Chokers don't do this because they cut you off at the neck (the way a round neckline does).

NOTE | You can make a choker look very attractive if you lengthen the chain to make it fall halfway between the base of your neck and your bust.

The only short necklace that is feminine is a very thin gold chain. A HEAVY WOMAN should avoid heavy necklaces such as big beads or large pendants because they draw attention to the bust. For a SMALL WOMAN a large pendant can add presence. As a general rule, long necklaces are preferable. However, a lot of dresses and necklines look sexier without them. Don't automatically think that a dress needs something because it's a simple design. To be sure, put on a necklace and look at yourself. Then take it off and look again. You will probably find that in most cases you're better off without it.

Bracelets

Women who wear bracelets give an impression of femininity and sexiness. If, when you think bracelets, you see heavy clunky ones that make noise – think again. There are very pretty bracelets that are neither showy nor noisy. I've been wearing fifteen $1/8$ inch gold bangles for years. Besides looking good they help my thin arms look less skinny. The wider mesh type of bracelet is very attractive too and can be worn for every day.

NOTE | Because bracelets draw attention to your hands, be sure they're well manicured.

For a HEAVY WOMAN only a few very thin bracelets will look good. They could be made from gold, plastic, or other materials, but they must be thin. For a SLIM TALL WOMAN there is no restriction except what is appropriate. For a SMALL WOMAN wide heavy bracelets are overpowering; she is better off with two or three medium ones or eight to ten very narrow ones.

Rings

If your fingers are long and thin, a big ring will look attractive, but if you have short fingers and a small hand, a simple band will look best. For short heavy fingers a medium-size stone will detract from the size of the hand. Make sure the ring is not so tight that it cuts into the flesh. These are only general guidelines; you have to see a ring on your finger to really judge its suitability. For women who don't wear rings at all, I should point out that a ring does dress up your hand and makes it look more attractive.

Not more than two rings should be worn on one hand. Anything more will make you look like a gypsy.

NOTE

Brooches

Sometimes a brooch can be just what you need when everything else fails. (They can be worn in many ways) on the lapel of my suit, to close and decorate a blouse; to hold a belt in place when it's worn around the hips, on a hip pocket, or on the side of a turtleneck; or at the depth of a V-neck. Please get out your brooches and see where they can do something for your outfit.

Antique Jewellery

The word 'antique' usually means high prices, but in the case of jewellery this isn't true. If you don't have many real jewels because you can't afford them, look for old pieces. Often you can find real gold or precious stones for a lot less than you'd pay for new pieces, and the designs are certainly more original. Other sources for antique jewellery are older family members, your grandmother and aunts, garage sales, and flea markets. It may take time to find something appealing but it's a great thrill when you do.

At this point I must confess that jewellery is for me what the

Don't be put off by a dull or dirty look. Cleaning can do wonders. I once bought a totally black pin for one pound. (I still see the woman's astonishment when I bought it.) After I cleaned it, it turned out to be a beautiful, real silver pin.

NOTE

French call a *folie* – so much so that I even buy pieces I can't wear just so I can hang them on the wall to admire.

General Hints

Coloured costume jewellery or jewellery with coloured stones should do one of three things: help coordinate your outfit, create a contrast with it, or complement your colouring.

- Whether you should wear gold or silver (real or not) depends on fashion trends and personal preference. A few years ago anything in silver was the craze; now gold is more dominant.
- There is such a thing as seasonal jewellery. Items and materials that are totally inappropriate and impractical in winter are very attractive in warmer weather: shells, wood, straw, flowers, and plastic. If you can't wear items like this in your daily life, use them for special occasions, but don't miss out on the fun.
- You need patience to find among your jewellery the piece that will look best with a particular garment. Sometimes it takes me longer to find the right chain or brooch than to get dressed! So give yourself enough time to select just the right accent.

Jewellery caters to a woman's greatest weakness, her vanity. And that is why, going far back in the history of any civilisation, jewellery has always been part of a woman – a part no woman should be without.

HOSE

Since a good pair of legs is always noticed, hose play a very important part in making you look your best. While the right texture and shade can do wonders, the wrong ones can be a disaster. (Although in this section I'll be talking mostly about pantyhose, remember what I said in Chapter 2 about the sensual appeal of stockings.) Finding pantyhose that do the most for your legs isn't complicated when you follow some basic rules.

1. If you're in the habit of picking up a pair here and there – in a cornershop supermarket, and so on, you'll end up with some pairs that look good and others that are unwearable. To avoid this, find a brand that fits you well and that comes in good

shades, then stick to it. (Cheap ones may be fine, but the colours tend to be ugly.)

> Most department stores now have their own brands. These are only a little more expensive than the supermarket types, but they are much better in quality with a large choice of shades. **NOTE**

2. The sheerer the look, the more natural and smooth your leg will appear. But if your legs have marks or little veins, more opaque hosiery is preferable.
3. Wear only sandalfoot stockings when your shoes are open or when you wear sandals.
4. Stay away from knee-highs if you want to keep your man. They are practical – but so ugly. I think if you want to get rid of a man, all you have to do is let him see you in knee-highs.
5. Textured hose are not very helpful when it comes to a sexy appearance. Usually they look heavy and project a sort of countrified image.
6. Hose with seams up the back (yes, they are coming back), all-over patterns, designs on the sides, or glitter should be considered only if you want to show off your legs. If your legs can afford the extra attention these details draw, by all means take advantage of them.

What Shades Are Best?

The shade you choose is influenced not only by your legs but also by the colour of your clothes. I'm not talking here about black versus dark green, but the finer distinctions between suntan and taupe. For example, if you're wearing a grey or black outfit, a taupe or slightly greyish colour would do more for your look than suntan.

The shade that is softest and coordinates with all other colours is the tone of beige closest to your own skin tone. However, if your skin is very pale, one shade darker will be better.

For a HEAVY LEG slightly darker shades are good. Matching the colour of your hose to your shoes will make the leg appear slimmer still. Stay away from thick tights, textured hose, patterns, designs, and glitter; they all make the legs look heavier.

For THIN LEGS stay with lighter shades (but not white). Sheer off-black hose are most unbecoming. Having thin legs myself, I know that they look like matchsticks in a black or off-black tone.

Practical Tips

- When experimenting with a new brand of pantyhose, buy only one pair.
- Try them on and when you're sure you like both their fit and colour, go back and buy more.
- If you have long legs, to assure a better fit and to make the hose longer, wet them before wearing them the first time. Pull on the legs and let them dry.
- Always wash your hose by hand. You can do it when taking your shower. Handwashing prevents snags.
- Keep an extra pair of pantyhose with you, either at work or in your purse. Runs happen to everyone, but they ruin your image for the rest of the day. If you count on dashing out to buy a pair, chances are you won't find any like those you co-ordinated with your outfit that day.

HANDBAGS

Since a bag is not worn directly on the body, it won't affect your look in any obvious way, but it will say something about your attitude. A square, stiff bag with short handles conveys a different message than a soft pouch slung casually over the shoulder.

A handbag is often referred to as a status symbol. This refers not only to its being expensive, but it can also mean:
- that you have taste
- that you have class
- that you're original
- that you're elegant
- that you're relaxed
- that you have a youthful approach to life.

Buying a bag can mean quite an investment. If you feel that you can't spend a lot on purses, limit your wardrobe to a few. I find that four to five bags is sufficient, not including an attaché case or briefcase. Since many women hate to change bags and carry the same one most of the time, a lot of purses never get used anyway. For every day buy one or two good leather bags in colours that go with most of your clothes. A neutral luggage-y shade of tan is versatile.

So is black, burgundy, or grey. This bag should be big enough to carry everything you need during the day.

NOTE | Too many women carry two or even three bags of more or less the same size. This makes them look like bag ladies.

You also need a medium-size envelope or clutch bag with a chain that will make it possible for you to wear it over the shoulder too. The fourth bag could be a small evening or disco bag, depending on your lifestyle. And you will probably need a straw or canvas bag for summer.

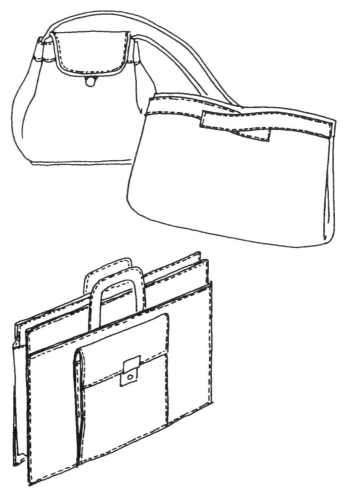

This minimum selection will allow you to buy really good handbags – the type you never thought you could afford. As with a dress, you will look better with the same good-quality bag every day than with several different cheaper versions.

<table>
<tr><td>NOTE</td><td>Handbags should always be made of leather (except your straw and canvas bag for summer). Don't buy vinyl or other leather substitutes. They may look all right when new, but nothing wears and looks like real leather.</td></tr>
</table>

A lot of working women need an attaché case or briefcase to carry business related materials. I am frequently asked, 'Can I carry a handbag as well?' For practical purposes you should. An attaché case alone really looks too masculine – and anyway, where would you keep your hairbrush and lipstick? Such items can be a nuisance when sharing a bag with the minutes of the last sales meeting. The bag with your personal belongings should be a shoulder bag that will leave your hands free. It should be small enough to be appropriate for a lunch date or to fit into the briefcase. The colour should be neutral and complement, if not match, your attaché case and shoes.

<table>
<tr><td>NOTE</td><td>For a sensual, youthful look pick a shoulder bag any time. It can be found in every style and type, even the most elegant and dressy.</td></tr>
</table>

Another frequent question is, 'Should my shoes match my bag?' It's not a must anymore, but by the same token you shouldn't wear a burgundy bag with brown shoes. The colours should at least complement each other: grey and black, blue and white, or bone and black. What does have to match is the style.

Don't wear a saddle bag with a dainty pair of high-heeled shoes, or gold sandals with a canvas bag. The type and texture should match.

For a bag to complement a woman's silhouette, it should be more or less in proportion to her body size. A small woman will look as awkward with an oversized bag as a big woman with a tiny clutch. So try to stay away from extremes.

FOOTWEAR

According to one man I know, the type of shoes a woman wears indicates how sexy she is.

Shoes

Before speaking of the sensual aspect of shoes, I would like to say that a woman's look is often spoiled by unflattering footwear. I know from experience that the most flattering shoe is not always the most comfortable and to combine the two is not always possible. If you walk to work you can't have a three-inch heel; you need a comfortable pair of shoes that will certainly look less flattering. But don't use your morning walk as an excuse. You can have pretty shoes in the office that you slip into when you arrive. Many women say that they can't wear a higher heel. The reason usually is that they rarely try.

You can get your feet accustomed to heels by first wearing a low heel (two-inches or so) only an hour or two a day, then gradually increasing the time span and the height of the heel.

There is no doubt that high-heeled shoes are always sexier than flat ones. But the high heels alone won't make them sexy. How well you walk in them is important too. When a heel is too high, throwing the body forward and causing imbalance, you won't look graceful; in this case a little lower heel will be better. Also, any shoe style is sensual only if it makes your legs look longer and slimmer.

Sexy Styles

Simple closed pumps, with heels 2½ to 3 inches high, are the most versatile for all occasions and dress styles. Because of their simplicity, they flatter the leg. A design with a slight cut-out on the side or in front is more delicate-looking. For a big foot, this break in the line will make the foot look shorter.

The slingback is also a very popular style. It is flattering to the leg because of the lack of bulk at the heel. This feature also helps it double easily as an evening shoe. The two-tone model in black and beige is a good choice for making your foot look smaller.

| NOTE | To transform a plain pump or slingback into an evening shoe, clip on a bow, pompom, or flower. I have even used earrings sometimes. |

Open strappy sandals are becoming only if your feet and legs are slim. The thinness of the straps will emphasise the size of the leg. Stick with a slingback if your legs are heavy. If a sandal exposes your toes completely, the result is not flattering.

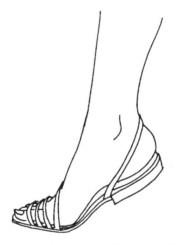

Straps look best when they cover half the toe, as shown here

The straps should cover the toes halfway. For sandals (or any other open shoe) you need smooth heels, polished toenails, and uncalloused feet.

| NOTE | When buying open shoes, ask for a half-size smaller than usual. Your heel and toes should finish exactly where the sole ends. If some of the sole is visible, the sandal won't look sexy, just too large. |

Wrong 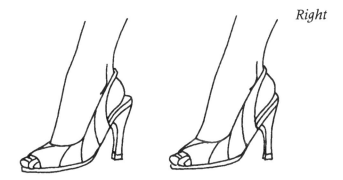 *Right*

Shoes more than other accessories should follow the fashion. Don't wear wedge heels and thick soles when slim heels are in. The latest shoe style can bring any dress up to date – but not the other way around.

To be able to follow fashions, restrict your shoe wardrobe only to those you really need. Who can wear eighteen pairs of shoes anyway? If you have that many (and I know women with more) they are certainly not all the latest style. Having three pairs for dresses and skirts, one pair for pants, two pairs of boots, one pair of silver or gold evening sandals, plus extras like summer sandals and slippers should be sufficient to cover most of your needs. This restricted number will also allow you to buy more expensive shoes.

Styles to Avoid

- Shoes with a flap or tongue. They shorten the leg and make it look heavy.
- Shoes with chunky heels.
- T-strap styles.
- Any style with a strap across the instep or around the ankle. The strap cuts the leg visually and lets it appear shorter.
- High-heeled oxfords ('nanny shoes'), except for wear with pants.
- Wedge heels.

Boots

Because they cover the legs completely, it's surprising that boots are one of the sexiest types of footwear – but again high heels are more sensual than low ones. Since a good pair of boots is quite expensive, they are a real investment. More than four years ago I tried on a magnificent pair of suede boots that cost £150. I was really put off by that sum and only agreed to take them when my mother offered to pay half as a birthday present. But I'm still wearing them and the compliments have never ceased. Expensive is always the cheapest.

To make boots wearable a long time, buy them in a conservative style and colour. You should also have a pair of rubber ones for rainy, slushy days. If you can afford a third pair, consider cowboy boots for the weekend. They look very sexy with jeans tucked in. A short pair of boots to wear with pants is another useful style. In the winter, pants look best when the foot is covered completely with a boot.

> **NOTE** Do you feel that boots are just for warmth? Ask your man how he feels about them. His response might make you wear boots, too. . .

Shopping Tips

- Buy your shoes or boots in the afternoon. You will get a better fit than if you buy them in the morning when your feet are still rested.
- When buying shoes to go with a skirt, don't try them on with pants, because you can't really tell how they'll look.
- Look at your total figure, not just at your feet. The shoes or boots you're trying on might not be suitable for the rest of your body.
- Look at footwear from the side. Does it make your foot look bigger?
- Don't let a salesperson tell you that stretching will make shoes or boots bigger. It rarely helps.
- To break in new leather shoes quickly, fill them with luke warm water. Empty them after twenty seconds, then wear them until they're dry.
  This process will make the shoes more supple and slightly bigger.
- Walk around with both shoes or boots on in the store. Try to find a spot without carpeting. This is the only way you can tell how well footwear fits.

By the way, I asked the man I know if his idea about shoes really works. He assured me that sexy shoes don't promise anything they don't deliver – and vice versa, clunky, heavy shoes never bring a surprise.

As an accessory, perfume is the last but not least important touch a woman has to add.

The magic of perfume has fascinated both sexes since the time of the Egyptians. It can speak without words. It excites, it flatters, it draws pictures, it seduces. Who then can be without it?

Perfume makes both men and women think of a beautiful female. Don't we all feel a little more glamorous after having added this most important touch? Maybe this is where part of its magic lies: it can make us feel prettier and more seductive even if we aren't beautiful. So you should wear fragrances not only for the benefit of others but also to increase your own awareness of your sensuality.

To the women who say they can't wear perfume because of allergies and sensitive skin, I would say keep trying different products until you finally succeed. No one can be allergic to everything. There has to be an exception among the hundreds of fragrances on the market today.

Getting the Most Out of Your Perfume

You can't apply a few drops of perfume after your shower or bath and expect it to last all day. You need to retouch it a few times during the day – say, every time you reapply your lipstick. Fragrances actually last longer than most women think – our nose gets so accustomed to an odour that we fail to be aware of it. Changing your perfume or alternating two scents might avoid this.

The best places to apply a fragrance are in front of your ear (not behind it because when covered by your hair it can't radiate), the nape of the neck, inside your wrists and elbows, and on the backs of your knees. Instead of applying it directly to the skin at the bosom soak a small cotton ball with perfume and slip it into your décolletage. You can further intensify the aura of your perfume by using bath products of the same scent: bath oil or bubble bath, soap or gel, body lotions, and bath powder.

Today one often reads about having a wardrobe of fragrances. Whether or not this is a plus is an individual decision. The important point is to choose a fragrance that you like. I have always felt it very reassuring and sensual to recognise a woman by her scent. It identifies her.

- Don't keep perfume for special occasions; use it daily. Once opened, it loses its potency and evaporates.
- Don't throw empty bottles away. Instead put them in your underwear drawer to give your lingerie a slight scent. when receiving a new fragrance as a gift do not open it. Try it at a counter tester in a store first.

If you don't like the scent you can exchange the gift or give it to someone else. Then you won't have a series of unused perfume bottles on your dresser. If your favourite perfume is too strong for daytime wear, use a toilet water or cologne in the same scent. The fragrance will be more discreet because toilet water and colognes are less concentrated. You can then reserve the heavier artillery for evening.

12

How Clothes Become Part of You

When clothes are truly A part of you, they will let your personality side emerge automatically. But for this to happen they must never be overpowering, either physically or mentally. They must be comfortable so that you don't feel self-conscious. Once dressed, you should be able to forget what you're wearing so that your mind is free to think of more important matters. You should not have to constantly adjust a scarf or straighten your skirt. You must know that everything is in place and will stay that way. Knowing this will increase your self-confidence and make you feel at ease.

In dealing with men, whether on a personal or professional level, it's very important to be relaxed and sure of yourself. Only then will they feel comfortable with you – the first step toward a good relationship.

We have all heard and know from experience that: 'There is no greater lift than looking good.' But getting this lift requires not only buying the right clothes but having a great deal of determination and personal pride. The American designer Halston once said that people who can't get it together are uninterested in themselves and lack self-respect.

In order to achieve your goal of looking attractive, the magic word is CARE. You have to care about your hair, your make-up, your hands, your figure, your budget, the type of clothes you wear and how to wear them. However, this attention should not result in a too made-up or arranged look. The effort must never show, even if it took you two hours to get dressed.

Of course, all this takes time, and time for many of us is a rare commodity.

But once you have made the initial effort, an hour a day should do it. You don't have an hour a day? I'm sure that your daily bath or shower plus your make-up takes at least half an hour, so all you need to do is rearrange your schedule a little to find another half-hour. That will give you a chance to wash your hair, apply another coat of nail polish, or iron a skirt. Spending this time regularly – and regularity is what counts – will make a great difference in your look. Being well-groomed has always been a plus. As I look around, I often notice that details like polished shoes or a well-pressed shirt would make all the difference.

YOUR FIGURE

For many years now we have been brainwashed into thinking that skinny is beautiful just because we see and admire flat-chested, narrow-hipped models in fashion magazines. It is indeed nice to be slim, but skinny is not a plus for everyone.

Gentlemen do not prefer scarecrows . A very thin woman may look well in clothes, but without them she doesn't offer much to hold on to. Of course, I'm not referring to someone who weighs 14 stone. But in the case of women 5 feet 6 inches tall, between one weighing 7 stone and one weighing 10 and a half stone, there are attractive alternatives. If being skinny is not the main objective, being in proportion (and firm) is.

During a visit to Brazil I admired the women there for their sensual bodies. On the beach I had a chance to see that their thighs were not thin and their bosoms were matched by round, firm derrieres. They were not slim, but what made them attractive and sensual was that they were well-proportioned.

If you are a size 12 on top and wear a size 16 around the hips, you have to do something about it. Exercise is the only thing that will correct this. Dieting alone will make you lose weight all over, whereas exercise will take off the bulk where you don't need it. Keep in mind that being well-proportioned is more attractive than having hollow cheeks and no shape.

> Being thin is no advantage when a woman gets older. She might even
> look older than she is when her skin starts to sag and her bones begin
> to show. In moderation a few extra pounds can take off several years.

YOUR BUDGET

Do you have a clothing budget? No? Then you should make one.
How else can you know whether you can pay £100 or £170 for a
suit – or whether you can afford one at all?

Knowing your monthly expenses and your income, you need to
set aside an amount for your clothing. Even if it's small, it will give
you some guidelines for quality and quantity. It will also overcome
the guilt feelings that make you say, 'Oh, I shouldn't have bought
that blouse' or 'I really went overboard this time.' When you have
sixty pounds a month to spend and you haven't bought anything
for two months, you can buy with a clear conscience; spending
forty-five pounds on a skirt won't seem extravagant. Since your
look is so important in how successful you are in any aspect of your
life, clothes are not vanity or coquetry. They are a necessity for
which you have to provide in your budget.

TYPE OF CLOTHES

The clothes I have discussed in this book will help you to dress to
impress. It's now up to you to adapt the designs that apply best to
your figure and lifestyle. While doing this keep in mind that you,
above all, have to like what you wear – first, because liking what
you wear will make you feel terrific, and secondly, since tastes vary,
you'll never please everybody. You might feel that your conservative navy suit and white blouse look good and appropriate, even
though a more fashion-oriented friend might say that you should
wear more flamboyant clothes. Because you can't 'please all the
people all of the time,' make sure that you please yourself always.

HOW TO WEAR CLOTHES

The nicest, most suitable dress can lose its effect and make you look
like you lack personality if it's not worn in the right way. Remember
my client whose husband didn't like her new shirtwaist dress? To
see how things are worn, how they look up-to-date, or how they

201

can project a younger image, check the fashion magazines. Then experiment on yourself and see how you look. Take the feather boa, for example; if it looks attractive on the model in Harper's Bazaar, why not on you? Following fashion trends in this way can help to make a garment look up-to-date. For example, when sleeves of jackets were worn pushed up, they made any blazer look more stylish. Turning up the collar of your coat or blouse will add a younger touch. Remember that how you wear your clothes is as important as what you wear – I would say even a little more.

HINTS

- Don't save a dress or other garments for a special occasion. Most of the time these events don't happen. Then you're left with a dress you haven't worn, or worse, you have missed looking as nice as you could have. Look GOOD every day. Think of now and not of what might come.
- Prepare for the next day. To avoid that 'thrown together' look, lay out everything that you intend to wear before you go to bed. If a button is missing, if your suit needs a little touch-up pressing, or if your shoes require polish, the night before is the time to do it. This is the best way to look well-groomed every day. It also allows you to dress without rushing or confusion. Use the extra time for your make-up or for a leisurely breakfast that will start you off on a better day.
- To be comfortable and at ease when wearing a garment for the first time, wear it a few hours at home before you go out.

MIRROR, MIRROR ON THE WALL

Do you have a full-length mirror? This is a priceless possession when it comes to your image – provided you use it.

Women have told me that they own such a mirror but that it's behind a door, in a closet, or hung in such a way that they can't really see themselves.

You can't know how something looks unless you see it. I've often thought something looked good until I saw in the mirror that I had made a mistake.

Regardless of what else you do in life, you will always be a woman and you must combine this fact with all other aspects of your life.

Don't let anyone tell you that your brains count more than your appearance. They count *as much,* and you should use them to improve how you look.